TRADITIONAL CHEESEMAKING
IN WALES

WELSH
CRAFTS

Traditional Cheesemaking in Wales

Eurwen Richards

Gwasg Carreg Gwalch

Cover design: Sian Parri
ISBN: 1-84527-047-9

Gwasg Carreg Gwalch,
12 Iard yr Orsaf, Llanrwst, Conwy, Cymru (Wales)
LL26 0EH
Tel: 01492 642031 Fax: 01492 641502
e-mail: books@carreg-gwalch.co.uk website: www.carreg-gwalch.co.uk
Printed and published in Wales.

Acknowledgements (illustrations, by page numbers):

National History Museum, Wales: 17, 27, 30, 49, 52, 53:

The author's collection: 22A, 26, 50

Gwasg Carreg Gwalch: 19, 22B, 29, 33-48, 75, 76, 80, 89-104

Llandyrnog/Corwen Creamery: 6, 7, 11, 13, 15, 61A, 68

Four Crosses Creamery – Derek James: 21, 61B

Johnstown Creamery – Bill Johnston and John Treharne: 57, 67

John Hughes, Llangernyw: 58

SCC, Chwilog: 62, 64-6, 86, 87, 92B

WDA food agency: 90B, 91A, 99B, 101A, 102A

Pant Mawr: 79, 98

Gorwydd: 93

Caws Celtica: 100A

John Donovan: 25

Contents

Acknowledgements

I wish to thank all those who have worked with or been involved in the cheese industry in Wales and share my passion for making this publication possible. I am grateful to the many, both on the farms and in the creameries, who have helped me delve into the past as well as make sure that my current information was as up to date as possible. Each of the present cheesemakers has been visited and many a happy hour has been spent with them, together with many former managers and staff of the various creameries.

I also acknowledge the assistance given me by the staff of various county libraries and record offices including those at Hawarden, Ruthin, Pembroke, Carmarthen and Bridgend, as well as St. Fagans National History Museum and the National Library at Aberystwyth.

Sprinking salt onto the curd as it is being milled; Llandyrnog, late 1930s

A Glossary of Welsh place-names

Anglesey	Môn
Glamorgan	Morgannwg
St David's	Tyddewi
Denbigh	Dinbych
Montgomeryshire	Sir Drefaldwyn
Carmarthenshire	Sir Gaerfyrddin (Sir Gâr)
Pembrokeshire	Sir Benfro
Caerphilly	Caerffili
Brecon	Aberhonddu
Radnor	Maesyfed
St Clears	San-clêr
Carmarthen	Caerfyrddin
Newcastle Emlyn	Castellnewydd Emlyn
Haverfordwest	Hwlffordd
Abergavenny	Y Fenni

Pasting the cloth bandage onto the Cheshire cheese at Llandyrnog, late 1930s

Cheesemakers and distributors of Wales

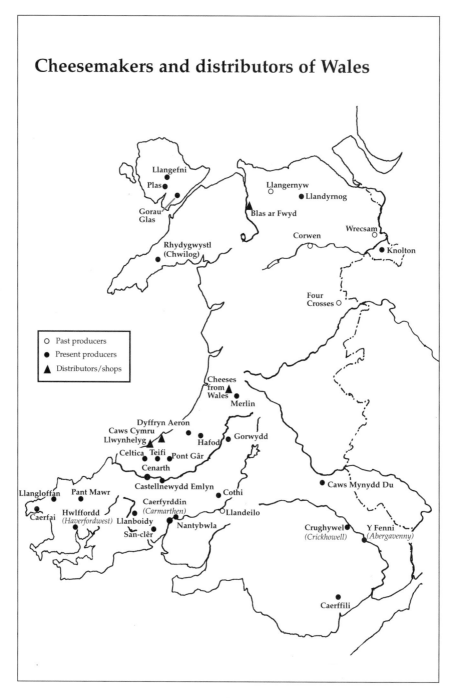

Llangefni
Plas ●

Gorau
Glas

Rhydygwystl
(Chwilog) ●

Llangernyw ○
● Llandyrnog

▲ Blas ar Fwyd

Corwen ○

Wrecsam ○
● Knolton

Four
Crosses ○

○ Past producers
● Present producers
▲ Distributors/shops

Cheeses
from ▲
Wales ●
● Merlin

Dyffryn Aeron ●
Caws Cymru
Llwynhelyg ▲ ▲
● Hafod
● Gorwydd
Celtica Teifi ● Pont Gâr
Cenarth ●

Castellnewydd Emlyn
Llangloffan ● Pant Mawr ● ● Cothi
Caerfai ● Hwlffordd
(Haverfordwest) Llanboidy ●
Caerfyrddin
(Carmarthen)
○ Llandeilo
● Caws Mynydd Du

Crughywel ●
(Crickhowell)
Y Fenni ●
(Abergavenny)

San-clêr ● Nantybwla ●

● Caerffili

8

Introduction

Cheese is a nourishing food that is found in many areas of the world: wherever humans have domesticated animals, animals' milk is used in one form or another. Cheese is made not only from the milk of cows, sheep and goats, but also for example from the milk of yaks, llamas, camels, reindeer and many other animals. There is therefore an enormous variety of types of cheese that reflect the animal whose milk is used, its food, and the method of manufacture.

Caerphilly is regarded as the cheese of Wales, but over the centuries many types and varieties of cheese have been made in the country. The north-east area of Wales in particular has been linked to Cheshire cheese. During the twentieth century, farmhouse cheese gave way to creamery production, and for many decades Welsh creameries were equipped with the latest technology, producing cheese of excellent quality. At that time Welsh cheese was labelled as 'English': the word 'Welsh' was quite unjustly seen as being indicative of an inferior product. Although most of the creameries making cheese in Wales have been closed, the cheese that is being produced today continues to be of the highest quality and is much sought after.

During the past thirty to forty years there has been a resurgence in small-scale farmhouse cheesemaking, and by now a variety of different types of cheese are being made in Wales. Many of these cheeses have received high accolades in competition both against cheese made in Britain and Ireland, and also against cheese made overseas.

There are many publications that list and describe cheese made throughout the world, including Wales, but in contrast this publication focuses exclusively on the cheesemakers of Wales, especially those making speciality cheese. It also provides the reader with a directory of sources and contacts.

Chapter 1

A brief history of cheesemaking

THE ORIGINS OF CHEESE

Cheese has been an important part of the human diet for many thousands of years. When animals were domesticated, their milk as well as their meat provided valuable food, and one way to preserve milk for longer was to make it into cheese. Cheesemaking involves curdling milk and conserving the solid portion (curds): it is this portion that is known as cheese.

Among the early pictorial evidence showing the curdling of milk there is a Sumerian relief from El-Ubaid, which dates from between 3500 and 2800 BC, and cave paintings from the Libyan Sahara that date from between 5500 and 2000 BC. Little equipment has survived, but it is thought that perforated pots dating from the Bronze Age were used in the making of cheese. References to cheese can be found in the Old Testament: in 1 Samuel 17.18, which dates from about 1017 BC, David is told to take 'ten cream-cheeses', and in Job 10.10, from about 1520 BC, Job asks: 'Did you not pour me out like milk, and curdle me like cheese?'

Cheese was a popular food at the time of the Roman Empire, and it became a well-known commodity in the territories occupied by the Romans. Some three hundred years after the Roman conquest of Britain, a treatise written by Palladius included advice on cheesemaking.

Much is owed to the monastic orders that flourished in Europe for the development of cheesemaking. They recorded cheese recipes and gained valuable knowledge about the cheesemaking process. In Britain the monks at Jervaulx Abbey and Fountains Abbey developed the Dales cheese, of which Wensleydale exists to this day. There is no evidence that this occurred in Wales, although cheese was regarded as a commercial product in the tenth century, as it is mentioned in the laws of Hywel Dda.

CHEESEMAKING IN WALES: TUDOR TIMES TO THE EIGHTEENTH CENTURY

Wales is a predominantly pastoral country with spectacular mountain ranges and lush lowland areas. Most Welsh cheese has been made from cow's milk although it was at one time common practice in some areas to mix sheep and cow's milk. There are occasional references during this period to cheese being made from goat's milk

In this land of small farms, the butter and cheese was mainly made for

The first load of cheeese from the cheese factory at the agricultural college, Lleweni in 1918, on its way to be stored and matured at Y Wern – the farm adjacent to the present Llandyrnog creamery.

home consumption. The industrialisation of areas such as the south Wales valleys and the movement of people from the land meant, however, that the provision of food for these urban areas became a necessity. The surplus stocks that were sold to provide added income soon became an essential part of the farm economy.

Minwel Tibbott records in her article on cheesemaking in Glamorgan that the Welsh Port Books of 1550-1603 illustrate the commercial importance of butter and cheese exports from many parts of Wales. Thomas Phaer reported as early as 1552 on the 'great lading of butter and cheese along the Glamorgan coast'. Minwel Tibbott observes that cheese was regularly exported from Cardiff to Bristol and the west of England in the early seventeenth century.

It is surprising that in the *Review of Agriculture in North Wales* of 1794, there is no mention of dairy cattle or of cheesemaking in the area bordering the English counties of Cheshire and Shropshire, although it is known that cheese was made there at the end of the sixteenth century. In contrast, the two counties of Cheshire and Shropshire are cited as having large and prosperous farms, and are credited with making the best cheese.

In a reference to the vale of Clwyd in his book *The Beauties of England and Wales*, which was published in 1812, J. Evans is complimentary about the quality of the pastures in the vicinity of the river Dee, and he comments that 'the article of cheese participates in the celebrity of the ancient county of Chester'. A Cheshire type of cheese made in Clwyd was exported to Chester and Liverpool. Although it was often regarded as being inferior in quality to that made in the English counties of Cheshire and Shropshire, the first prize for the best Cheshire cheese was awarded to William Jones of Pistell Farm, Hope, near Mold, at the Royal Liverpool, Manchester and North Lancashire Agricultural Society Centenary Show in 1867.

It was common practice well into the twentieth century to skim the milk, make butter from the cream, and make cheese from the skimmed milk. Whole or unskimmed milk was only made into cheese for the richer folk or for special market purposes. The practice of skimming the milk was mainly for economic reasons, as butter was the more profitable product, and cheese could still be made from the skimmed remainder. With hand-skimming, there would have been enough fat left in the milk to make a reasonable-quality cheese, but with the advent of the mechanical separator, little fat was left in the milk. The quality of the cheese therefore varied considerably, depending on the efficiency of the skimming process.

In an article on 'The Agriculture of Pembrokeshire' in 1887, W. Barrow Well comments that 'the cheese of Pembrokeshire when compared to Cheddar is of second rate quality. It is as a rule deficient in fat being made from skimmed milk.' Whatever such perceptions about quality, a substantial quantity of cheese was on occasion offered at auction.

J. Evans, who published observations of his travels in Wales in a volume entitled *Letters written during a tour through South Wales*, comments in his seventh letter on the 'State of Agriculture in Glamorganshire', and observes that: 'where butter is a staple commodity you must not expect the cheese should be of prime quality. The cheese made in South Wales is inferior and sought after by the Welsh to eat it when new. If kept it will be hard.' He also mentions the practice of mixing cow's and sheep's milk, and remarks that the cheese which results, if matured, is 'little if at all inferior to the boasted Parmesan'. According to him, 'cheese made at Ewenny sells for one shilling per pound while that of the dairies about St. Fagans brings sixteen pence'.

THE NINETEENTH AND TWENTIETH CENTURIES
The agricultural and industrial revolutions saw a burst of scientific knowledge about and change in farming. The improvements in cattle, in pasture, and of winter feeding all affected the milk that was produced.

Early days at Corwen

Little in the cheesemaking process changed, however. Until well into the latter half of the nineteenth century, it continued to be a craft that was practised with little scientific understanding of the processes involved, but there were individuals who saw how scientific knowledge could be used to advantage. One such person was Joseph Harding, who was born into a cheesemaking family in Somerset in 1805. Harding was a reformer and travelled widely all over Britain. He particularly saw the need to ensure that home-produced cheese competed favourably with the increasing quantities of imported cheese. Although his efforts were not greeted with enthusiasm in all places, the *Ayrshire Advertiser* published a treatise written by him on 'The Practical Aspects of Cheesemaking' on the 29th of July, 1859.

During the nineteenth century, the Royal Agricultural Society of England became very concerned about the need for agricultural education and training. Informative articles were published in their journals, and they also published a series of pamphlets on the practice of cheesemaking. The advice given by George Gibbons is typical of the time: 'The first essential is pure sweet milk of good quality ... the dairy and its surroundings must be scrupulously clean ... the udders and teats of the cows and the hands of the milkers, must be thoroughly washed before milking.' The need for good hygiene was well understood, and when it came to the milk delivered to the factories, as the creameries were then called, good hygiene was insisted upon.

Although in 1794 George Kay reported that Welsh farmers were 'indolent and inactive', it is clear that they were as much involved in these changes and improvements as those across the border.

There was a great deal of experimentation during the later half of the nineteenth century to produce a better and more consistent cheese, and the more successful ones began to get established as named varieties. However, the making of cheese continued very much to be a skilled craft, and the ability of the individual cheesemaker remained of paramount importance.

During the nineteenth century there were vast movements in the Welsh population – for example with the development of the coal mining valleys in southern Wales. The population of Cardiff increased from 1,870 in 1801 to 32,954 in 1861, and in the area there was a corresponding increase in the demand for Caerphilly cheese. M. Tibbott reports that miners were prepared to pay 7d per pound for Caerphilly cheese rather than buy American cheese at 3d per pound. American cheese was a type of Cheddar and was not regarded as a good quality product.

The practice of grading and branding Caerphilly cheese began during the last decade of the nineteenth century. In Caerphilly, where cheese fairs and an annual show were held at the Market Hall, Mr Edward Lewis, caretaker of the Market Hall, would sample the cheese, and if he found it to be of standard quality, would mark the product with the official stamp. Grading took place at the Market Hall into the twentieth century, but no one replaced Mr Edward Lewis after his death in 1909.

The amount of farmhouse cheese that was produced declined rapidly in the early years of the twentieth century, as farmers found it more profitable to sell their milk into the liquid trade. Direct rail links to London and other large cities from rural areas such as Llangefni in northern Wales and Whitland in southern Wales were established, along with milk collection depots, and some of the depots were developed so that they could make butter or cheese on site when there was surplus milk. Cheese was made at Four Crosses and Pensarn, for example, while butter was made at Llangefni and Pontllanio.

However, in many hill areas away from such improved transport links, farmhouse cheese continued to be made well into the twentieth century. In his work *The Great British Cheese Book*, Patrick Rance describes the cheese made by Mrs Ceinwen Davies of Gwybedog Farm, which was one of the fifty-four homesteads that lay on the Epynt Range in Powys. In

Prize cheese winners (Corwen) with the cheesemakers
and presses in the background

1940, this large tract of land was requisitioned by the government for military training, and to this day it remains a military training ground. To make a Caerphilly type of cheese, Mrs Davies mixed one gallon of sheep's milk with the milk from two cows – one batch skimmed, and one unskimmed. The cheese was matured for at least two months, and often for as much as six months. Any that was surplus to home requirements was sold at Llanwrtyd or kept for the November Brecon Fair.

THE MILK MARKETING BOARDS
The national emergency that occurred with the first world war changed the fortunes of British agriculture. During the first world war (as also occurred during the second), the British farmer became the major supplier of food, and saved the population of the British Isles from starvation, but after the first world war came the slump of the 1920s, followed by the depression of the 1930s. The farming and dairy industry was in a situation of near-disaster. It was the establishment of the Milk Marketing Boards that enabled many a farmer to survive, and the story of this slump and

survival should not be forgotten as we become ever more reliant on imported rather than locally-produced foods.

The Milk Marketing Board of England and Wales commenced operation in October 1933, having been set up under the authority of the 1931 Agricultural Marketing Act. It controlled marketing of all the milk produced in England and Wales. In essence it was a compulsory co-operative of dairy farmers backed by statutory authority. Similar boards were set up later in Scotland and Northern Ireland.

War-time controls severely restricted the quantity and type of cheese that could be made in the UK during and after the second world war. Imported American cheese often became the only cheese that was available during the period of food rationing and, whatever its quality, it was appreciated. The term 'American' is still used in some areas of southern Wales to describe a mild Cheddar cheese.

War-time controls ended in 1954, and it became possible to make cheese again in the UK. Many of the west country Cheddar makers also made Caerphilly cheese, both before the war and after the controls had been lifted, and much of that was exported to Wales.

The Milk Marketing Board supported the making of farmhouse cheese and fostered the growth not only of traditional varieties such as Cheddar and Cheshire, but also new types of cheese. By the 1960s, some two thirds of the creamery cheese made in England and Wales (as opposed to farmhouse cheese) was made in Wales, and until the late 70s and early 80s few if any farms made cheese other than for home consumption. In the late 70s and early 80s there was a new interest in the discovery and revival of traditional cheese varieties, but Caerphilly cheese continued to be made by west country Cheddar makers such as Greens of Glastonbury, Barbers of Ditcheat and Duckett of Wedmore. (The latter remains the only maker of traditional Caerphilly cheese in 2006.)

Wholesale producers of milk and farmhouse cheesemakers within the Milk Marketing Board of England and Wales (no separate figures available for Wales)		
Year	Total wholesale producers	Total farmhouse cheesemakers
1939	95,412	1,121
1945	131,254	221
1950	143,019	129
1955	138,305	126
1960	121,376	221
1965	99,219	279
1970	79,011	237
1975	58,532	293
1980	42,725	249

Farm owners and cheese factory workers at Plas Du, Chwilog c. 1918

In 1984 quotas were imposed on milk producers in an attempt to restrict the amount of milk being produced in Europe. Any production in excess of the stated quota was subject to a financial penalty. This was an incentive to diversify and make farmhouse cheese again, rather than tipping excess milk down the drain.

In 1986 the Milk Marketing Board listed all the on-farm makers in England and Wales and this included many who had rediscovered traditional cheese varieties as well as the established makers of Cheddar and Cheshire. The combined output of farmhouse cheese had increased by 1986 to over 10% of all the cheese made in England and Wales.

Following increasing criticism that the Milk Marketing Board was an outmoded organisation that did not conform to modern competitive requirements, the Milk Marketing Scheme was revoked in 1994, and the industry deregulated. For the first time in sixty years, farmers were free to sell their milk to whomsoever they chose, but this did not prove to be the panacea that many had wished for. In spite of increasing costs, producer milk prices have continued to be driven downwards, and the period since deregulation has been one of more uncertainty and further decline in the dairy industry.

Chapter 2

The past twenty-five years

THE REVIVAL OF FARMHOUSE CHEESE

The past twenty-five years has been an exciting period, with a new cheese industry developing in Wales. The wide range of cheese reflects the landscape and the legacy of centuries of farming. This landscape, from the mountain ranges of Snowdonia, Pumlumon and Preseli, to the lush pastures of Anglesey, the Vales of Clwyd and Glamorgan are more than areas of outstanding beauty.

Consumers are seeking varied tastes and textures, and are finding them in local and regional produce. Welsh farming is encapsulated in farmhouse cheese, which is made in the traditional way from the milk of the area. Welsh farmhouse cheese is highly regarded, and many of the new varieties have achieved great acclaim in both national and international competitions.

However, it is a difficult and changing market. Some cheesemakers have failed to make a commercial success of their venture and have given up. Others are no longer making cheese because of the constant and ever-increasing problem of satisfying bureaucratic and regulatory requirements.

It was during the 1960s that Pamela Grisedale began what was unfortunately to become a failed enterprise with her herd of goats in Nebo, Cardiganshire. She produced a new cheese called Haminiog, a small 8-10lb hard raw milk cheese. She also made a soft cheese. The main problem was selling the products: local sales were small, and selling at places such as agricultural shows did not provide a regular return. There were fortnightly deliveries to Wrexham, the Wirral and Manchester, all of which were a considerable distance from Nebo. Hers was a vision that proved not to be commercially viable at that time.

In 1982 her enterprise was included in the following listing of farmhouse cheese and cheesemakers:

Ty'n Grug – a raw cow's milk Cheddar type made by Dougal Campbell
Llangloffan – a raw cow's milk Cheshire type made by Leon and Joan Downey
Haminiog – a smallholder raw goat's milk cheese made by Pamela Grisedale
Porthrhiw – hard and soft raw goat's milk cheese made by Mark and Gill Tennant
Marianglas – a soft raw goat's milk cheese made by Jean Rickford

Of these, the only one that has survived is the Llangloffan cheese, and by

18

Leon Downey behind the counter of his farm shop at Llangloffan

2006 Joan and Leon Downey had also passed the baton on.

Two years later, in 1984, the imposition of milk quotas caused many an old item of cheesemaking equipment to be rescued, and many traditional cheese recipes to be resurrected. However, traditional Caerphilly was already being made at the Four Crosses creamery before the resurgence of farmhouse production. Although Four Crosses was a creamery, it was smaller than some farmhouse units in England that made Cheddar and Cheshire. The Caerphilly at Four Crosses was made from pasteurised milk and in the traditional way, but it was produced on a large scale to meet the standards and demands set by the supermarkets – packed as a 4kg wheel for the supermarket delicatessen counters, or as 18-20kg blocks for cutting and prepacking as was required for the supermarkets. In comparison with the traditional Caerphilly of farmhouse production, this cheese tended to be more acid and crumbly and was sold to be consumed at a few weeks of age.

By 1986, Welsh cheesemakers listed in the Milk Marketing Board directory included Caws Cenarth, Glynhynod and Peter Sayers Farmhouse Caerphilly, along with Duckett's Somerset Caerphilly. There were other Welsh farms making Caerphilly at the time, such as Maesllyn, Nantybwla, and Pantyllyn.

Many new cheese names and types were also created during this revival period. Those that have not survived include Ty'n Grug, Pantyllyn, Felin Gernos, Waungron, Maesllyn, Caws y Felin Cheddar, St Florence, Sir Benfro, Penbryn, St. David's, Caldey Abbey Cheddar, Nevern Cheddar and Heritage Cheddar. St. David's was a washed-rind cheese, a type of cheese that has been said to smell of dirty socks. When it was selected by a supermarket, they required a form of packaging which contained this natural smell and interfered with the maturing process. This then also destroyed the cheese.

Although many soft cheeses were made for local sale and were not known to many people, there were exceptions, including Rhosygilwen, Pencarreg and, later, Celtic Brie and Celtic Blue, all of which are now only historical names. Pencarreg cheese and Ty'n Grug were developed by Dougal Campbell, who was tragically killed in a farm accident on August Bank Holiday in 1995. His passion, vision and knowledge has been passed on, however, and continues with other farmhouse cheesemakers in England as well as Wales. Rachel's Dairy bought the company, but the Pencarreg cheese did not survive the death of its creator.

Later casualties have been Pen y Bont, a hard goat's milk cheese, and sheep's milk cheeses such as the Little Acorn Products made by Karen and Don Ross; Cwmtawe Pecorino and others of the typical Italian style made by Giovanni Irranca in the upper regions of the Swansea valley; the Maesmor range, and Yan Tan Tethera, a cheese based on the Pyrenees type.

This list may give a false impression that farmhouse cheese is on the decline. While some makers do decide to retire, others begin anew. Two new makers began their ventures in 2006, for example. The Carmarthen Cheese Company will continue the Llangloffan recipe and will also make other varieties, while Hafod, a new cheese, will be made by Sam and Rachel Holden at Bwlchwernen in Llangybi. This cheese will be to a recipe similar to that of Ty'n Grug, and will thus continue the tradition established by Dougal Campbell.

Most of the new cheeses have been made from cow's milk, but more varieties are being made from the milk of goats, sheep and even water buffalos. At present, buffalo milk is made into cheese outside Wales, but this may change in the future.

Small-scale production has its problems, and the picture is a rapidly changing one. There is a greater variety of Welsh cheese now available in supermarkets than ever before, but they have to compete for space and on price. While some speculate that with the increasing dominance of the supermarkets there will be no small shopkeepers in our high streets by

Four Crosses Creamery
Top left: milk off-loading bay with tanker of milk being off-loaded
Top right: wrapping a 18kg block of cheese for maturing after taking out of press
Bottom left: starter culture being added to milk in a vat with mechanical stirrers
ensuring all is thoroughly mixed together
Bottom left: the railway siding which was used to take the liquid milk, with the creamery
buildings alongside

2015, customers will continue to seek out interesting and varied regional cheeses. In this context, the importance of specialist shops and in particular of farm shops and farmers' markets cannot be emphasised too strongly.

A group of dairy students at Pen-coed Farm Institute 1927.
Author's mother is the second on the left in the front row.

Llysfasi Agricultural College, near Ruthin

Chapter 3

Education and training

Although the University College of Wales, Aberystwyth (as it was known until recently) is the oldest constituent college of the University of Wales and became the centre of excellence for dairying, the first courses in agriculture and dairying were held at the University College of North Wales, Bangor.

Three dairy schools were established by University College of North Wales: at Sylfaen near Welshpool in 1889; at Lleweni Hall near Denbigh in 1889, and at Bangor in 1890. Cheesemaking classes were held at Sylfaen and Lleweni. Examinations were held by UCNW Bangor, and certificates and prizes were awarded to the successful students. The 'ordinary certificate' covered the production and properties of milk, together with the basic science and practical task of making cheese. The 'advanced certificate' course followed a more in-depth study of the subject.

There were also travelling schools, with a fully-equipped dairy that enabled demonstrations and teaching classes to be held in places such as village halls and chapel vestries, with the instructresses (the instructors were always women) taking their equipment from one place to another.

In 1891 the first courses in dairying, with practical instruction in the making of cheese, were established in the Agricultural Department of the University College of Wales, Aberystwyth. The college also offered local training by peripatetic instructresses in the travelling dairy schools. Agreement was reached between the colleges that Bangor would run the classes in northern Wales to include part of Montgomeryshire, and the remainder of Wales would be organised by Aberystwyth.

This was a period of awakening in rural education and the dairying classes were very popular. These courses ensured that the skills of buttermaking and cheesemaking were retained, but also ensured that there was a better understanding of hygiene and of basic chemistry and bacteriology. My mother was one of the many young people in Glamorgan who attended classes at Pencoed during the 1920s. Although she never made cheese on a commercial scale, it was her knowledge and skill that kindled my interest in cheese.

The following table provides a picture of the numbers of students who undertook some form of training in Carmarthenshire alone from 1891 to 1899.

STUDENTS ATTENDING DAIRY EDUCATIONAL CLASSES IN CARMARTHEN FROM 1891 TO 1899		
Year	Number of students attending dairy schools schools	Number of students attending advanced dairy
1891 to 1898	1,936	187
1898 to 1899	175	17
Total	2,111	204

Dairying education and training has undergone many changes since those early days. In 1964 the Farm Institutes at Llysfasi and Glynllifon in northern Wales, and Gelli Aur and Usk in southern Wales offered one-year courses in dairy husbandry and allied subjects. Two technical colleges – the Denbighshire college at Wrexham and Pibwrlwyd Rural College in Carmarthenshire offered day-release courses that enabled candidates to qualify for City and Guild Certificates in milk treatment, processing and control.

Advanced courses leading to the National Dairy Diploma and degree standard were conducted at the University College of Wales, Aberystwyth until the department was closed in 1967. That closure was soon followed by the other colleges and institutes.

Following the decision to close the dairy department at Aberystwyth, a decision was taken to offer a course at the Monmouthshire College of Agriculture at Usk, which would enable students to sit the National Dairy Diploma examination. That qualification was subsequently phased out, with the last examination held in August 1973. A three-year sandwich Ordinary Diploma course in food technology commenced at Usk in 1975, but it was short-lived.

There are now no diploma or degree courses in dairy science or technology anywhere in the United Kingdom. Those universities that still offer food science include varying amounts of dairy teaching. At Reading University, for example, which used to be an old and established centre of dairy and cheese excellence, some cheesemaking theory is included in the 'commodities and food proteins' lectures, with a few 'processing practicals'.

Food Centres have been established at Coleg Menai and Horeb, but the occasional two- or three-day course in practical cheesemaking at these places cannot be compared with the education that was provided a century ago. One cannot help wondering where the next generation of cheesemakers will come from.

THE ROLE OF WOMEN

Making cheese was long ago considered to be the work of the farmer's wife and daughters. The dairymaid was also an important figure: she was expected to milk the cows as well as turn her hand to making butter and cheese. On the larger farms, dairymaids were often employed from the local village, but the advent of the Milk Marketing Board in the 1930s changed this role, when it became more profitable to sell the milk itself rather than cheese.

In spite of the advances in agriculture, little changed in the process of cheesemaking until well into the twentieth century. All the education and training was geared to the dairymaid. The peripatetic instructresses were indomitable women and their influence was widespread. Although the increasing number of creameries employed men, in the 1960s at least three of the head cheesemakers were women. At that time the Ministry of Agriculture, Food and Fisheries had women heading their five ADAS regions as Dairy Husbandry Advisors (these five regions of ADAS, or the Agriculture Development and Advisory Service, covered England and Wales).

The situation has changed during recent decades. Men have taken over the role of cheesemakers, especially in the modern creameries, and more men are also to be found making farmhouse cheese. The dairy industry has thus experienced a curious reversal of the modern trend of women taking over roles formerly occupied by men, for here men are increasingly taking the role formerly filled by women.

Newcastle Emlyn creamery, 1936

Ewenny Pottery, the oldest pottery in Wales, still occupyies the same site and has been run by the same family since before 1800. Today it is owned and run by Alun and Jayne Jenkins and daughter Caitlin. There has not been a kiln large enough for bowls of this size since around 1920s. Above: daughter Caitlin and father Alun with two large bowls typical of those in general use, with modern pottery in the background. Below: two pottery bowls, useful for general purposes and for making cheese for home consumption on farms in the Glamorgan area.

Chapter 4

Cheesemaking

The making of cheese on a small scale remains very much a skilled craft, although more of the science behind the process is now understood. The basic ingredients required to make cheese are milk; a microbial culture (a starter) or an acid (such as lemon juice or vinegar) to sour the milk; rennet or other coagulating enzyme, and salt. Other products that provide increased variety can be added, such as colour or herbs, but these are not essential for cheesemaking.

Curds and whey form when milk is soured by microbes. The curds (the solids), when separated from the whey (the liquid), result in a soft cheese with a limited shelf life.

Curds can also be produced by the action of rennet. There are many stories as to how rennet was discovered. One story recounts how an Arab was carrying milk in a dried sheep's stomach as he travelled through the desert, and found that the milk had curdled. These curds made better cheese than that which could be obtained by the natural souring of milk.

The practice of keeping curd for a day and mixing it with fresh curd

Milking cows out in the fields

occurred in some areas of Wales, especially when there was insufficient curd from a single day's milking to fill the mould and press it into the cheese shape. Traditional Lancashire cheese, which is made by mixing together the curds of more than one day's milking in this way, is recognised as a good cheese for toasting, but although the mixed curd produced by some Welsh farmers would also have made a good toasting cheese, no references have been found to show that it was used as such.

Small variations in ingredients and during the making of cheese all aid the creation of different cheeses and different cheese types. Recipes are available for every variety, and each is carefully monitored in both large- and small-scale production. It is easier, however, for the small-scale maker to adjust the recipe when local variations are more apparent, as for example occurs when milk quality changes from season to season. This is where the skilled craft of the maker becomes more apparent.

MILK SUPPLY

The native cattle of Wales were a dark brown or black colour, ancestors of our present-day Welsh Black breed. There was a difference between the cattle of northern and southern Wales: those of the north were more of the beef or draft type, and are described in 1794 by C. Hassall as being 'unprofitable to the pail'. The cattle of southern Wales were more typical of dairy breeds. C. S. Reed mentions in 1849 that the coal black Pembrokeshire breed are 'capital milkers providing ten quarts per day or less of rich milk'. However in his book *Cattle*, published in 2000, Twm Elias cites William Youatt, who stated in 1834 that the Pembroke cow was a better meat than milk animal. This supports the speculation that the type and characteristics of animals found in Wales before the twentieth century varied greatly.

The Glamorgan breed, which was said to produce a lot of milk – and thus also butter and cheese – for the industrial towns of southern Wales, is now extinct, but it was thought to be similar to the Old Gloucester breed. This Old Gloucester breed has been revived and produces milk well suited to cheesemaking.

The present-day dairy herds are composed mainly of Friesian cattle, although other breeds are also kept. It is from the only rare-breed herd of Red Poll cows at Cilowen Farm, for example, that Llanboidy cheese is made.

Some traditional breeds of Welsh sheep, such as the Llŷn and the Llanwenog, are noted for their prolificacy and their abundant milk production. These and others are known to have been milked and the milk made into cheese well into the twentieth century. Present-day sheep dairy farmers tend to rely on imported breeds such as the Friesland. All the animals were milked by hand half a century and more ago. Nowadays most are milked by machine in milking parlours.

There is evidence of the use of goat's milk and the making of goat's milk cheese in areas of Pembrokeshire at the beginning of the twentieth century, but such cheesemaking was very local and was not as significant as sheep's milk cheese. The situation has changed over the past few decades, and Welsh goat's milk cheese is now well known and highly regarded.

The milk of sheep and goats differs in its composition from that of cow's milk, and people who have an intolerant reaction to cow's milk and cow's milk products can usually drink the milk and eat the cheese made from both sheep and goat's milk.

One very noticeable difference between sheep and goat's milk cheese when compared with cow's milk cheese is its colour. Cows that graze on lush green pastures rich in clover produce a creamy yellow milk. This is due to two colour components in the milk: one is riboflavin, which is found in the serum; this gives whey its greenish tinge. The other is

A Glamorganshire cow

Cheese moulds with followers (lids) typical of those used for Caerphilly cheese

carotene, a carotenoid pigment in the milk fat. There is a high level of carotenoid in green grass, which is why there is a yellow colour in cow's milk. Sheep and goats do not transfer these carotenoids to their milk, and consequently their milk and the products made from that milk are very much whiter than cow's milk and cow's milk products.

STARTER CULTURES

In previous centuries it was the natural souring of milk that provided the cheesemaker with the bacteria needed to make cheese. This practice was fraught with danger. There was little control of the cheesemaking process and the end product could contain undesirable pathogens. In the late 1890s, cultures of lactic bacteria replaced the use of sour milk or the previous day's whey as cheese starters.

Nowadays, starter production is a separate and highly sophisticated industry. Commercial companies can provide single or multiple strains of organisms suited to the specific requirements of the cheesemaker. The choice of organism depends on the variety of cheese and to some extent on local traditions. Bacteria such as *Lactococcus lactis* sub-sp. *lactis* and *Lactococcus lactis* sub-sp. *cremoris* are among the organisms normally selected for cheese varieties such as Caerphilly and Cheshire. Starter cultures convert the lactose (milk sugar) into lactic acid. This is the first stage of cheesemaking, and provides the right conditions for it to proceed.

When it was stored in cellars or damp places, cheese used to often develop a natural internal mould. One farmhouse in Glamorgan was widely known for its blue (mouldy) Caerphilly cheese. The farmhouse was on the side of a hill, and the cheese store was effectively underground, which provided perfect conditions for the development of a blue cheese. As occurred with the choice of bacteria for starter cultures, the same care has been taken in the selection of mould species from those that may be found naturally, and the production of such selected moulds now also forms part of the industry that supplies the particular needs of the cheesemaker. Strains of *Penicillium roquefortii* are used for the internal mould of blue cheese, and *Penicillium candidum* is used for the white surface growth.

COAGULANTS

In addition to a starter to sour the milk, cheesemaking requires some kind of coagulant. The lining of the stomach wall contains enzymes that coagulate milk, and as animal stomachs were frequently used to carry liquids, it was found that the milk carried in this way curdled, and made a longer-lasting cheese.

These stomachs could have been those of any of a variety of domesticated animals, but while some countries continue to use rennet obtained from lamb or kid stomachs, it is calf rennet that has been and still is the most important coagulant for cheesemaking. A Danish company named Chr. Hansen A/S has produced rennet commercially since 1840, and this product remains the standard against which all other coagulants are measured. When commercial rennet was difficult to obtain, it was not unusual for the farmhouse cheesemaker to cut into strips the washed fourth stomach (*abomasum* or *vell*) of a milk-fed calf, and place these in a salt solution, which extracted the coagulating enzyme. Occasionally the strips were placed directly into the milk. The stomachs of young lambs were also used in this way.

The crude stomach-wall extract is called rennet, and the enzyme prepared from it was called *rennin*. However, to prevent confusion between this and the enzyme *renin*, which can be extracted from the kidney, the name has been changed to *chymosin*. The enzymes obtained from the stomach of lambs and kids are the preferred coagulant for some varieties of cheese that are made from the milk of these animals.

Partly as the result of a shortage of animal rennet during and after the second world war, other sources of coagulants were sought. Some plant extracts or juices will coagulate milk, but the cheese that results is often of a poor quality. In the nineteenth century, Lady's Bedstraw *(Galium verum)* was called the 'cheese-rennet herb', and was used in Cheshire to coagulate milk. These coagulants react in a different way to animal rennet and were only used when rennet was not available. However the Cardoon Thistle *(Cynaria cardunculus)* is still used to make a type of sheep's milk cheese in Portugal.

During the second half of the twentieth century a range of microbial coagulants became available, all of which meet the needs of vegetarians, and little animal rennet is now used in the UK, although it is still the preferred coagulant in Europe. The microbial coagulating enzymes are derived from various organisms including moulds such as *Mucor meihei*, bacteria such as *Bacillus subtilis*, or yeasts such as *Klyveromyces lactis*.

These coagulants form the 'junket' or 'gel' that is the first stage in the formation of a cheese curd. The cheesemaker is able to select from a wide range the best coagulant for the particular variety of cheese that is to be made, and for the market that is to be served.

SALT

Salt is an ingredient that has gained an unpopular profile in modern food-production, but its use is an essential part of the cheesemaking process. When the whey is separated from the curds, the curds begin to mat together to form the cheese. Variations in the handling and treatment of the curd at this stage contribute to the vast array of cheese varieties that are available.

For a cheese such as Edam, for example, the curd is moulded in its final form or shape immediately after the whey has been removed, which gives it its rather rubbery texture; the cheese is then immersed in a brine bath to provide the required salt content.

In contrast, in the making of Welsh and British types of cheese, the curd is 'textured'. After the curds have matted together they are cut and turned according to the needs of the particular cheese variety that is being made, until the curd is ready to be salted and moulded into the shape of the final cheese. If dry salt is used, it is added at this stage. Salt inhibits the growth of lactic organisms, and slows down the rate of acid development; it thus helps to control the process of cheesemaking as well as determine the final cheese flavour.

It is also possible to add salt by placing the whole cheese in brine (as with the Edam-making process described above). Caerphilly cheese can be either brine-salted or dry salt can be added to the textured curd at the moulding stage. The choice of method lies with the maker.

*Box cheese press at the heritage
centre, Scolton Park, Haverfordwest*

Box cheese press at Ceredigion Museum

Advanced certificate awarded at University of Wales, Aberystwyth

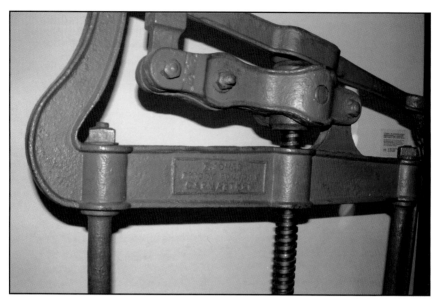

A cheese press from the Priory Foundry, Carmarthen, now at the National History Museum of Wales, St Fagan's.

Old style dairy

Round vat at Penbryn imported from Holland, a type used by many small-scale farm-house cheesemakers at the beginning of the twenty-first century.
Top: warming the milk
Bottom: cutting the curd (junket)

Filling the moulds. The curd is not textured for the Gouda type of cheese as it is for the Caerphilly and Cheshire varieties.

Cheese moulds in press. Note the modern plastic moulds.

Cheese moulds taken out of press, cheese removed, turned out and placed upside down...

...back into mould for pressing again for a short while.

Cheese taken out of press and trimmed...

...before being placed into brine.

Cheese store

*Traditional Welsh
breeds.*

*Above:
a Glamorganshire cow.
Right:
a Pembrokeshire cow.*

A modern outdoor rotary milking parlour at Cefnamwlch, Llŷn

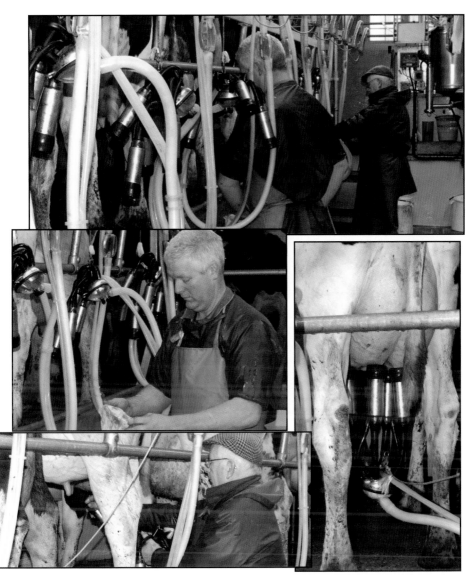

A modern milking parlour at Plas Newydd yng Ngharnguwch, Llŷn.
Top: cowmen in the pit preparing the cows for milking – cleaning and massaging the
udders. Middle left: moving down the line, wiping the udders clean before the teat cups
are placed. Bottom left: the teat cups being placed on the udder. Bottom right: the cow
being milked. The milk is sucked out of the teat by vacuum and then transferred to the
bulk tank via a pipeline.

A typical rural scene at Plas Newydd yng Ngharnguwch with Friesian cows in the foreground and a tanker collecting the milk.

The tankers' yard at SCC, Chwilog

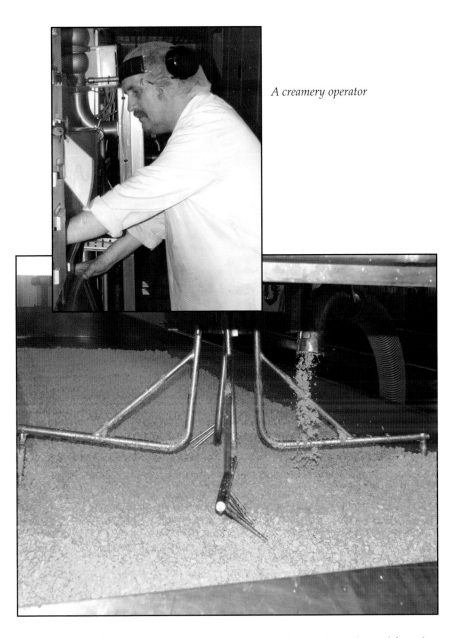

A creamery operator

Making coloured cheese at a creamery. The curds and whey are being dropped from the vat onto a lower level. The whey is drained away enabling the curd to be textured in a shallower vat (table).

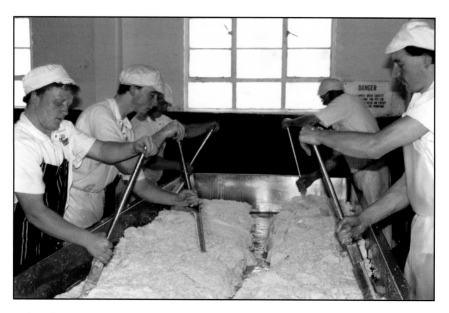

Cutting the curd after draining the whey at Four Crosses Creamery, 1970s

A later stage in the process of making Caerphilly cheese at Four Crosses

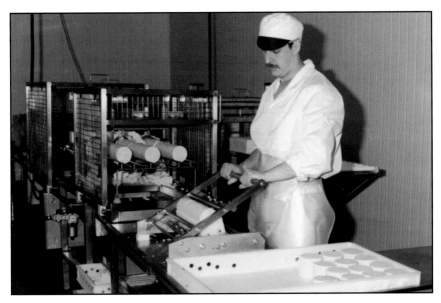

Cheese being formed and cut into the required size before being waxed

Salting the curd by hand

Hand waxing cheese

The old style gang presses at Llandyrnog creamery in 1950s

*Cheese in plastic moulds being turned at Four Crosses Creamery,
with gang presses in the background*

Aeron Valley Cheese Creamery

Llandyrnog Creamery

45

A disused milk stand with old and disused milk churns

Young cheese on a modern stainless steel cheese rack in a special store for mould-ripened cheese

The farmhouse home of the original Llangloffan cheese

General view of Gorwydd farmhouse and the whitewashed entrance to the cheesemaking room

Carwyn Adams of Caws Cenarth replacing the lid on the brining tank with cheese in the tank

Paula van Werkhoven in the Teifi cheese store

Celtic Promise and Saval in the cheese store at Caws Teifi

Cheese competition at the Royal Welsh Show at Builth Wells

Caerphilly stamp used by Mr Edward Lewis at Market Hall Caerphilly

COLOURING AGENTS

Although most people prefer the natural colour of cheese, many do not realise that colour variations in cow's milk cheese derives mainly from the diet of the cow. Colour affects the consumer appeal of cheese, and in some areas a 'coloured' cheese is preferred.

Various amounts of annatto, a yellow-red colour obtained from a South American shrub, *Bixa orellana*, are used for coloured cheese varieties. More annatto is added to the milk for a deeper-coloured cheese such as Red Leicester, whereas less is added for the lighter-coloured Double Gloucester. The addition of colour has no effect on the cheese flavour, but its use – and the quantity used – is very much dictated by consumer demand. Cheshire and Cheddar cheese are made both with and without the addition of colour, and in some areas, such as in Scotland, the coloured versions are preferred.

Other colouring agents may also be used, such as chlorophyll when sage is an added ingredient in a cheese. Chopped sage leaves turn brown, and when it is used on its own it gives the cheese an unappetising appearance. The addition of the green colour enhances the appearance of the cheese. Sage used to be frequently added to farmhouse Caerphilly cheese, providing variety in the diet of the household. It would either be included as a sandwich layer or would be mixed through the curd. There are also examples of sage leaf patterns on the surface of the cheese. The green colour used to be obtained by squeezing the juice from chopped cabbage or spinach leaves, but nowadays there is extensive legislation controlling all the ingredients used in cheesemaking to ensure the product is safe to eat, and like all added colours, the chlorophyll that is used today must be from the list of legally permitted additives.

WHEY DISPOSAL

During the process of making cheese, approximately 80% of the initial volume of milk is left as whey. The composition of whey varies considerably, depending on the original milk and on the type of cheese made from that milk. Whey is a valuable food and was at one time a major source of food for pigs: although it contains a great deal of water, it can contain around 1% of protein and 4.5% of lactose.

It was common for the farmers who took milk to the first cheese factories to return with their churns filled with whey. During the 1960s, whey from the Newcastle Emlyn creamery was shipped to a large herd of pigs at Clynblewog farm, near Trelech. As the creamery expanded, it produced a greater quantity of whey to be disposed of, which the pig herd could not accommodate. The pig industry is a notoriously cyclical one,

'A modern system illustrating the heating of milk for the manufacture of Cheddar cheese'
– an illustration in the Royal Agricultural Society of England leaflet on The Practice of Cheddar Cheese Making by George Gibbons, 1892.

and the herd was dispersed when the situation became commercially unviable.

The childhood rhyme in which Miss Muffet sits eating her curds illustrates a vital stage in the process of making cheese. Whey proteins are heat sensitive, and when whey is heated the heat-labile albumin and globulin are destabilised and precipitated. Today these whey proteins are more commonly associated with the Italian Ricotta cheese. However, in many areas of rural Wales whey or buttermilk was mixed with oatmeal or oatmeal bread and eaten while harvesting or as an evening meal. The whey protein curds are a light texture and form an appetising as well as nutritious human food.

Whey contains a variable amount of fat that can be separated and made into butter, which is also often known as 'farmhouse butter'.

In Wales, other means of using whey have been developed to dispose of the very large quantities that are produced in the modern cheesemaking plants. For example, the milk sugar lactose can be removed and manufactured into galactose/glucose syrups for the confectionary trade. Many cheesemaking units have whey protein concentration and extraction plants, which utilise the recovered water and make the protein available for use as a valuable nutritious food for both humans and animals.

A large company named Volac International Ltd established a manufacturing facility for whey at Felinfach in the Aeron valley in 1989. From concentrated whey protein they make high-quality feeds for calves, lambs and piglets. They also produce concentrated lactose. This is an example of modern technology being used in conjunction with an old and well-established cheesemaking industry.

EQUIPMENT
The equipment required to make cheese on a small scale has changed little over the years. The basic requirements are a container for the milk; a thermometer to check temperatures; a knife to cut the junket; a means of testing the developing acidity; the means to break the curd into small pieces and salt it once it is to the desired texture, and the moulds in which to press it.

A container to hold the milk is a major item of equipment. This can be as small as a bucket or as large as a modern cheese vat containing many thousands of litres of milk. Any form of container can be used to make cheese as long as it is clean and can be cleaned. The pottery at Ewenny in Glamorgan used to make large earthenware bowls that were used for many purposes in the farm household, including cheesemaking. A surviving example is similar to that utilised by my mother when she used to make Caerphilly cheese, and is around a hundred years old. It is probable that similar types of locally made containers were used in other parts of Wales.

The orthodox cheese vat was rectangular, made of tinned or stainless steel, and often had an outer jacket to hold hot water. It is now difficult to obtain small vats, and during the past few years some of the small farmhouse cheesemakers have installed round vats from Holland.

Moulds or hoops are required to shape the cheese while it is being

A seventeenth-century wooden box type cheese press used in Whitland

pressed. The size and shape are determined by tradition: Caerphilly, for example, is traditionally a small wheel, while a Cheshire used to be a large cheese of 60 to 80 pounds in weight. The material used for cheese moulds has changed over the years, from traditional wood, to tinned steel, then stainless steel, and is now plastic. Many of the old presses that used to be part of cheesemaking on farms have been found and have been put to use again.

Economic factors often influence modern developments. The 'blockformers' that are used by the larger creameries have replaced traditional cheese moulds and presses. With these blockformers, the curd is compacted under vacuum, and this provides a block of cheese of a specified shape, size and weight. This suits the demands of the prepacking industry and of supermarkets.

An eighteenth-century cheese press from Tyddyn Siôn Wyn, Talsarnau using a large stone boulder as

A cast-iron lever cheese press from Llangadog.
These presses can be seen in use today.

Chapter 5

Product safety

RAW MILK

The subject of product safety and whether milk should be pasteurised or not is one that has been ongoing for many decades. In the past, when bovine TB was considered to be the most dangerous pathogen in milk, milk was heat-treated to ensure the destruction of the tubercle bacillus *(Mycobacterium tuberculosis)*. *Mycobacterium tuberculosis* was used as the 'index' organism for pasteurisation: the heat treatment that destroyed the bovine TB pathogen also destroyed all other pathogens that were found in milk. More recently, other pathogens have emerged, and more intense heat treatments are being promoted to ensure consumer safety.

Regular testing and eradication schemes ensured that by the early 1950s, all the cattle in Carmarthenshire and Cardiganshire were declared attested areas that were free of bovine TB. This was earlier than any other area in Wales or England. Pembrokeshire was an eradication area in 1954, and the counties of Brecon, Radnor, Montgomery and Meirionnydd were declared eradication areas in 1955. The bulk of cattle in Wales were therefore considered free of the disease by the mid-fifties.

In 2006 the situation is quite different, with southern Wales being one of the areas noted in England and Wales as 'hot spots' for bovine TB. Incidences of the disease are being increasingly reported throughout Wales. The arguments about the source of this disease in cattle, and the need or otherwise to cull wildlife in order to control it, are contentious. It is sufficient to say that bovine TB is a serious disease and causes great concern, especially when valuable animals have to be destroyed.

Bovine TB is not the only concern with respect to raw milk products, however. In February 1989 the then-Minister of Agriculture announced his intention to ban the sale of cheese made from raw milk, because there had been a Listeria scare, and it was thought that the pasteurisation of milk would ensure a 'safe product'. Before the 1980s, *Listeria monocytogenes* was known to cause disease in animals, but the 'Listeria hysteria' at this time created disproportionate concern in the general public when certain foods, including cheese made from raw milk, were implicated as vehicles of infection in humans.

The proposed ban precipitated the birth of the Specialist Cheesemakers Association, whose main aim was and still is to preserve and extend the wealth of excellent farm-made cheese, while ensuring it is safe to consume. During the past fifteen years a Code of Best Practice for small-scale cheesemakers has been agreed with the various Regulatory Authorities, which includes a system to ensure its implementation. The code is a valuable resource for the small-scale cheesemaker: it ensures that standards of safety and quality are maintained, and it provides a necessary reassurance to the consumer.

While pasteurisation does kill the more common pathogens, contamination can occur during the process of cheesemaking. This is why there is a need for good hygienic practices at all stages of the process. There is therefore no justification in insisting that a farmhouse cheesemaker pasteurise the milk that is taken directly from healthy animals. However, where there is the possibility of bovine TB in the area, many a farmhouse cheesemaker has taken the wisest course and pasteurises the milk. This ensures that the product is safe as far as the bovine TB pathogen is concerned, and it prevents the potential condemnation of cheese stocks by the regulatory authorities.

FOOD HYGIENE REGULATIONS

The first regulations dealing with the adulteration of food were passed in 1860. Milk was a food that could be easily adulterated – for example by the addition of water. The Milk and Dairies Order of 1926 was the first real legislation that was introduced to try and protect the public from fraud as well as to establish hygiene standards.

Since those early days, the quantity of legislation aimed at protecting the health of the consumer and the prevention of fraud, as well as other aspects such as the packaging and labelling of foods, has become almost an industry in itself.

Since the UK became a member of the European Community in 1973, legislation that has been agreed and adopted among the member states has been applied here. This legislation increased with the completion of the internal market programme in 1992, when many more Directives and Regulations were incorporated into UK legislation.

The Food Safety Act of 1990 updated the primary legislation that was in force at that time, and also provided for more controls. As a consequence of devolution, in 1999 the controls pertaining to food hygiene and standards became the responsibility of the Welsh Assembly Government.

The latest regulations, The Food Hygiene (Wales) Regulations 2005, which came into force on the 1st of January 2006, consolidate seventeen European Union measures in the food hygiene area into just two measures. The regulations are similar to previous ones, with some additional requirements, such as the need to have procedures in place based on Hazard Analysis of Critical Control Points.

The primary aim of this increasing raft of legislation continues to be food safety and the protection of human health. Nothing has changed in this respect for over a century.

General view of vats with overhead stirring equipment in a twentieth century creamery

Chapter 6

Creamery cheesemaking

HISTORICAL ASPECTS

Many of the Welsh creameries began as joint farmer ventures, few of which were initially successful. The history of Welsh creameries – or factories, as they were initially known – is an interesting story, of which the following is only a brief summary.

Cheesemaking on a factory scale began in America in about 1851, and with better means of freight transport, large quantities of cheese began to be exported to Britain. The first English cheese factory was established in Longford, Derbyshire in 1870. Within a few years there were a large number of factories making cheese, including some in the border area of north-east Wales.

One of these, the Aldford Associated Cheese Factory, lay on the

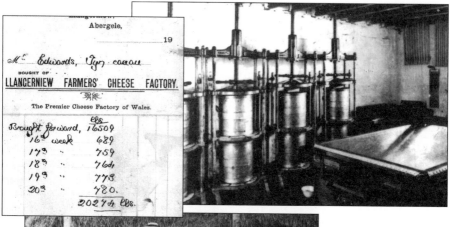

Abergele,

19

Mr Edwards, Tyn coaau

BOUGHT OF

LLANGERNIEW FARMERS' CHEESE FACTORY.

The Premier Cheese Factory of Wales.

	lbs.
Brought forward,	16509
16th week	689
17th "	759
18th "	764
19th "	778
20th "	780.
	20274 lbs.

Llangernyw and Llansannan Cheese Factories
Top left: an example of the Llangernyw factory's invoice. Top right: Cheshire cheese in press. Middle left: Llangernyw cheese factory workers. Middle right: Cheshire cheese in the maturing store. Bottom: dairymaids at Llansannan, c. 1921.

58

English side of the border but received milk from Welsh farms. The factory operated from the 1st of April until around the 20th of November and by 1894 was well established. Each farmer member was expected to work at the factory if called upon to do so by the Association Secretary. The farmers signed an agreement to that effect and if they failed to comply they were fined.

In spite of the development of these cheese factories the total amount of cheese made in Britain declined, and by 1911 only 18% of the cheese consumed in Britain was home-produced. The early decades of the twentieth century were difficult, and many of the factories that were established during these years did not survive.

Most of the early cheese factories developed as an extension of farmhouse production. One was established at Hafodunos in Llangernyw in 1916. Another, in a building set aside for the purpose, was opened in June 1921 at Cross Keys Farm, in Llansannan. Local farmers brought their milk to these factories and took the whey back to their pigs.

Four Crosses Creamery, in the old country of Montgomeryshire, was situated about a mile from the English border. In 1910 Messrs Reeces of Liverpool were receiving milk from local farms at Four Crosses. Between 1911 and 1913, some of this milk was made into cheese, an enterprise in which the sons of local farmers assisted. In 1913 the new creamery was officially opened as the Four Crosses branch of the Cheshire Milk Producers Depots Ltd., but in 1925 it went into liquidation.

From 1925 till 1944 it operated with the assistance of local farmers, but in 1944 it was sold to R.W. Griffiths of Forden (of National Milk Bars fame), who in turn sold it to the Milk Marketing Board in 1957. For many years, Cheshire and Caerphilly cheese varieties were made in both block and traditional forms at Four Crosses, using traditional methods.

A number of small creameries developed in Carmarthenshire in the late nineteenth and early twentieth centuries. In around 1890 the Vale of Towy Dairy in Ffairfach, Llandeilo was probably among the first to make cheese and butter. This dairy was moved to another site in St. Clears, and later, in 1928, the Mutual Dairy Company began making cheese in the Pensarn Road factory. In the 1920s Johnstown was established as a farmers' co-operative on the outskirts of Carmarthen to manufacture butter and casein. It was owned variously by Cow & Gate, Unigate and Dairy Crest. In 1972 it was entirely re-equipped to make cheese and could rightly claim at that time to be the largest and most modern cheese creamery in the UK. Whereas other places had one-tonne presses, Johnstown was the only creamery that could mature cheese in one-tonne stainless steel blocks.

In 1920 a farmers' co-operative started at Aberarad in Newcastle Emlyn, in an old building which had served as workhouse and which had subsequently been occupied by Danes felling timber for the 1914-18 war,The co-operative ran into difficulties during the recession of 1926, and in 1932 the premises were bought by Dried Milk Products, a subsidiary of Cow & Gate, who developed the site into a modern cheese creamery. Caerphilly was the first variety of cheese made there in 1933, followed by Cheddar in 1937. Since then it has been owned by various companies. In 1971, under Unigate, a new cheese room was commissioned with the latest mechanised equipment. The creamery was closed by Dairy Crest, but subsequently reopened to make Mozzarella cheese, and is now owned by Dansco.

A new modern creamery that made cheese and other products was opened by Dairy Crest at Maelor on the outskirts of Wrexham in 1976. It closed as a cheese manufacturing unit in 1993, but the site has since been developed as one of the more advanced cheese-packing plants.

During the 1960s and 70s there was considerable investment in the latest cheesemaking equipment and technology in Wales. This was when Welsh creameries both large and small were to the fore, and were making large quantities of very good quality cheese. This reputation and continued investment to ensure good quality cheese continues with the remaining creameries, which are at Llandyrnog (owned by Dairy Farmers of Britain), Chwilog (South Caernarfon Creameries), the Aeron Valley (owned by Lactalis UK) and Haverfordwest (owned by Dairy Crest & First Milk).

Until well into the 80s it was the practice to sell cheese manufactured in either England or Wales as 'English' cheese: cheese labels and all the advertising referred to 'English' cheese even though it might have been made in Wales. This is no longer the case, as the law now requires that it be possible to trace the source of the product, and Welsh cheese can be and rightly is named as such.

CREAMERY CHEESEMAKING IN THE PRESENT
There are several creamery cheesemakers still operating in Wales, some of which have gained strong reputations for their products. The creamery at Haverfordwest was owned at one time by Kraft, and the Cheddar that was made there was matured and packed in Liverpool as 'Crackerbarrel'. The present owners are Dairy Crest, who bought the creamery from Unigate in July 2000. **Haverfordwest Cheese Ltd,** as the creamery is now known, makes a range of Cheddars from local milk supplied by First Milk. Their Afon Cleddau Cheddar has gained a reputation as a

A typical rural scene before the 1950s – collecting milk churns in the Corwen area

Milk tankers at Four Crosses. Milk churns can also be seen.
The lids of the right hand tanker are open.

Offloading churns and tipping the milk at a creamery stage in the 1950s

A 1940s milk churn collection lorry,
owned by South Caernarfon Creameries, Rhydygwystl, Chwilog

premium-quality cheese Cheddar.

A butter and skimmed milk drying creamery was built by the Milk Marketing Board at Felinfach in the Aeron valley in 1957. It was expanded in the 1970s and closed in 1988. Following that closure, a cheesemaking unit was built on land adjacent to the original creamery, and cheesemaking began there in 1989. The whey from the cheese creamery is piped directly to the Volac International Ltd factory, now established within the former butter and skimmed milk powder creamery. In 1997 **Aeron Valley Cheese** was sold to Milk Marque, then in 2000 to a joint venture of First Milk and Dairygold (the latter an Irish co-operative). In 2003 it was sold to A. McLellands and Sons (a Scottish company) and in December 2004 it was again sold, this time to Lactalis UK, a France-based multi-national company.

The creamery continues to make mainly Cheddar cheese but has also gained a good name for the quality of its Double Gloucester and Red Leicester varieties. The packing plant, which was originally part of the manufacturing creamery, was continued as a separate unit by Dairygold, but was closed in 2006.

In the late 1920s the Vale of Clwyd creamery was opened as a farmers' co-operative to make butter. Cheese manufacture was transferred from a local farm a little while later. It was closed during the early 1930s, reopened in 1935, and acquired by the Co-operative Wholesale Society (CWS) in 1947. A major reinvestment financed the complete rebuilding and re-equipping of the creamery, which was completed in 1976. At the time, this made it one of the most advanced creameries in Europe.

The name was changed to Associated Co-operative Creameries, Llandyrnog and it continued to benefit from further investments and improvements. The latest, in 1990, ensured that the creamery stayed at the forefront of cheese manufacture. One achievement at that time was a World Champion award for a mature cheddar.

The creamery was purchased by **Dairy Farmers of Britain** in August 2004. Their aim is to continue investment, and to further develop the high standards of the creamery's previous owners.

A farmer-owned co-operative called the **South Caernarfon Creameries Ltd** Rhydygwystl, Chwilog was established in 1938 at Chwilog to process milk collected in the Llŷn Peninsula. This was one of the only two such co-operatives in Wales, the other being Hufenfa Meirion, which is now closed. South Caernarfon Creameries is owned by its producer members, each of whom is represented on the Board of Directors. The creamery has expanded, and to satisfy manufacturing requirements milk is now collected from much further afield – from the

*Eifionydd Co-operative at the beginning of the twentieth century,
the forerunner of South Caernarfon Creamery*

*Filling the block cheese mould with milled salted curd in the 1960s. In the background
the weight of the curd in the mould is being checked and would be adjusted if necessary.*

Aberystwyth area, for example, and from the Denbigh area.

South Caernarfon Creameries has enjoyed far-sighted management, which has been supported by its Board of Directors. There has been continual investment since the first cheesemaking equipment was installed in 1959. The latest investment is to ensure that the creamery conforms with EU Environment Directives. The main variety of cheese it produces is Cheddar, but the creamery is equally known for the quality of its Leicester, Double Gloucester and Monterey Jack cheese. Old Shire is a specially selected vintage Cheddar waxed in a distinct green-coloured wax to retain its freshness.

Glanbia Cheese Ltd at Llangefni used to be a butter-manufacturing creamery, but now it makes Mozzarella cheese for the pizza market. It is owned by Glanbia, an Ireland-based international dairy processor.

After the closure of the creamery at Newcastle Emlyn by Dairy Crest in 1983, limited use of the site continued until it was acquired by McCain in 1988. In 1989 they began making Mozzarella cheese for the pizza trade. The creamery was sold to **Dansco Dairy Products Ltd**, and they continue to make Mozzarella cheese at this site. Mozzarella forms an important part of the 'industrial' cheese market.

Packing Cheddar cheese in film before placing it in a box for maturing, 1960s

General view of cheese vats with overhead cutting and storing equipment at SCC, 1960s

BRANDED AND INDUSTRIAL CHEESE

A group of farmers who wished to market a range of locally-made cheese launched the **Snowdonia Cheese Company** in 2001. The company markets a premium range of cheeses, some natural, others with additives, that are sold in small 200g waxed minis or 3kg waxed wheels. The original 'Black Bomber' is an extra-matured Cheddar selected from cheese made at an established creamery of renown in northern Wales. Snowdonia cheese is an excellent marketing concept which promotes the best of Welsh produce.

Collier's cheese memorialises a piece of southern Wales history. The south Wales valleys were noted for the quality of their coal, and the men who went underground to dig this 'Welsh Gold' worked hard in hazardous conditions. Although there are no longer any working mines in the valleys, there are still many families who retain vivid memories of the coal-mining era. The originator of Collier's brand of Cheddar recalls how his father and grandfather worked in the mines and how they appreciated a good powerful Cheddar cheese, as well as the more delicately-flavoured Caerphilly. The concept of Collier's is in part a memorial to the miners and the mining culture of the south Wales valleys.

Collier's is matured for at least eighteen months to give it a very strong, slightly sweet and pleasantly lingering taste. The pack design is

Johnstown Creamery
Top: *general view of Johnstown creamery in the 1970s with the cheese vats on the upper deck, the tables where the curd was textured on the lower deck, with the milled curd being passed along the belt to the tonne moulds.*
Bottom left: *the milled curd being dropped into the moulds.*
Bottom right: *a general view of the tonne moulds.*
Middle: *a typical creamery cheese store of the latter half of the twentieth century. The cheese blocks are contained in slatted wood.*

dramatic, with the face of a collier who is wearing a pit helmet, against a black background.

Cheese is increasingly used as an ingredient in many other foods, and **Ash Manor Cheese Company Ltd** in Wrexham has been supplying those needs since 1993. As customers have demanded better quality and more natural cheese, new techniques and innovative production methods have been developed. As well as pre-sliced cheese being available, cheese is also used extensively in ready meals as a diced, grated and shropped product. The last, shropped cheese (a cross between shredded and chopped cheese) is indicative of the innovation necessary to satisfy the demands of the customer. While Ash Manor relies extensively on Welsh cheese, they also supply a range of cheese types and varieties as a service to the food sector.

CWS creamery Corwen. Left hand: coal boilers.
Middle: hand-tipping of milk churns into weighing bowl.
Right: milk-holding tanks with operator looking into one through its 'window'.

Chapter 7

Present-day farmhouse cheesemakers

There are currently in the region of 2,600 milk producers in all of Wales. In 1964 there were 2606 producers in Cardiganshire alone, with a grand total of 12,137 in Dyfed. By 1984 the number in Carmarthenshire had decreased to 1,894, but to this day it remains the most productive dairy area in Wales, followed closely by Pembrokeshire. Most of the farmhouse cheesemakers of today can be found in this southwest area of Wales.

ABERGAVENNY FINE FOODS LTD.
When Pam and Tony Craske retired from working overseas, they looked for a house with a few acres of land in Wales, and found Pantysgawn Farm on the Bloringe mountain – a derelict house with no water or electricity, but with captivating views. To one side there were trees and the Usk valley; to the other an expanse of moorland down to Blaenavon, which is now a World Heritage site.

Like so many ventures, their cheesemaking began by chance. It was difficult for them to obtain a fresh milk supply while they proceeded to work on making the place habitable, and they bought a goat. One goat was followed by more goats, so that whereas there had been insufficient milk, now there was an excess. What better to do than make the excess into fresh cheese?

It was a steep learning curve making and selling the cheese, but it proved to be a very successful venture, as Pantysgawn cheese is now to be seen in most supermarkets as well as in specialist shops. Planning permission to expand production at Pantysgawn was refused, as the farm lies within the Brecon Beacons National Park, and in 1990 the on-farm production moved to Castle Meadows Park, an industrial site on the outskirts of the town.

The identity and quality of the product has not diminished. Pantysgawn is a lovely smooth textured fresh goat's milk cheese with a slight lemony flavour. Indeed some of the judges at an international cheese competition were convinced that cheese of this quality could only come from France. A range of Pantysgawn goat's cheese, plain or with added ingredients is available, although the most popular product remains the plain cheese.

This family company continues to expand. Among the more well-known products are the blended cheeses such as Y Fenni (Cheddar with a mustard seed blend), Tintern (Cheddar with chives and onion), Harlech (Cheddar with horseradish and parsley) and others. An extensive range of snack foods such as breaded Camembert is also now being made. Where possible they use and promote local ingredients.

Abergavenny Fine Foods may not seem to be typical farmhouse cheesemakers, but theirs is a story of enterprise and success, overcoming as they have the constraints imposed by operating originally within the restrictions of a National Park.

CASTLE DAIRIES CAERPHILLY

This unit on the Pontygwindy Industrial Estate began its existence as a liquid milk bottling plant. At the time it was purchased by John Lloyd, there was little incentive to make cheese. However, following the increased interest in traditional cheese varieties, it was decided in the late 1980s to make Caerphilly cheese in the area once more. Old recipes were researched and traditional cheesemaking equipment was purchased, enabling the cheese to be made using traditional methods.

John's son Nigel now runs the business. The milk is sourced from local farms, which not only provides exact traceability but adds to the tourist attraction of the area – it is a Caerphilly cheese made in Caerphilly from Caerphilly milk. The cheese has a creamy, slightly open texture and a mild, very slightly salty flavour. Although the recipe follows that which was popularly made in the area for many years, this latest version – the traditional 3.5 kg wheels and the mini 400g cheese – is waxed in a green-coloured wax. This was initially intended for the tourist trade, but by now it has achieved a Castle Dairies identity. The local Council has been very supportive from the beginning, and the various tourist events hosted by the borough ensure that Caerphilly cheese is very much on the agenda.

Other products are also made at Castle Dairies, some of which are for the dairy ingredients market, and this is also one of the few remaining units making Welsh butter in Wales.

NANTYBWLA FARMHOUSE CHEESE

Nantybwla farm is situated a few miles outside the town of Carmarthen, a town that has grown around the river Tywi as it flows toward the estuary and Cardigan Bay. This is a rich fertile dairy-farming and milk-producing area.

It was the imposition of milk quotas in 1984 that caused Edward and Eiddwen Morgan to research recipes and begin making traditional Caerphilly cheese at Nantybwla. Some of Eiddwen's forebears attended the dairy and cheesemaking classes at Aberystwyth, and the

70

cheesemaking concern therefore constitutes a continued historical link.

The cheese made at Nantybwla is typical of a young fresh Caerphilly, although on occasion a more mature cheese is available. The delicate but rich flavour reflects the pastures on which the pedigree herd of Jersey and Holstein cows graze, as well as the quality of the milk they produce.

The traditional Caerphilly is made in 4.5kg wheels and, as was the tradition, is supplied in its natural rind. The smaller versions are waxed. The range has been extended to include other varieties, such as a soft cheese and a type of Cheddar, as well as Caerphilly with added ingredients.

A Welsh Cheddar promotional leaflet

Nantybwla farmhouse cheese, like all those made in this area of Wales, have achieved high acclaim and won many awards at national and international competitions.

COTHI VALLEY GOATS

The Cothi, a tributary of the Tywi, rises many miles beyond Cilwr Farm. After passing Talyllychau Abbey and driving up the narrow roadway near to the farm entrance, it seems as if the visitor has arrived at the top of the world. It is a wonderful view across the valley, to the Brechfa forest on one side and Mynydd Mallaen on the other. There is open country as far as the eye can see and it is no wonder that Lynn and Richard Beard fell in love with the place.

The family moved from Kent with their five hundred goats, a milking parlour, cheesemaking equipment and household effects in August 2003. They milk around 320 goats and make a range of cheese. Richard originates from a place called Storrington, and one of their hard cheeses, which is matured for about six weeks, bears this name. Two soft varieties, Luddesdown Log and Twayblade, are young fresh cheeses but are full of flavour. Caws Talley is comparatively new to the range. It is covered with a white mould and, when ripe, has a soft creamy texture.

These are only a few of the cheeses made at Cilwr farm. For some time after moving to Wales, Richard continued to take cheese (and kid meat when it was available), to the Borough market in London. His regular customers commented on the improved quality, and the richer flavours. According to Richard, these improvements can only be attributed to the pastures and the quality of the Welsh water that the goats now enjoy at Cilwr farm.

Cothi Valley Goats is very much a family enterprise, with children Laura and David and grandparents Mary and Fred Jeffrey all lending a helping hand when and where necessary.

GORWYDD FARM

Gorwydd is typical of a small Welsh farm in mid Wales. It nestles on the side of the lower reaches of the Cambrian mountains overlooking the Teifi valley. A mile or so up the road is the village of Llanddewi Brefi, and further on lies Tregaron and the famous Cors Caron.

Todd Trethowan spent some years learning the art of cheesemaking with Dougal Campbell, Chris Duckett (who makes Caerphilly cheese in Somerset), and others, before establishing himself at Gorwydd in 1996. Since then, Todd Trethowan has been joined in the business by Maughan and his wife Kim. Gorwydd Caerphilly is now a well-known cheese both in Wales and internationally.

Although the Trethowan brothers came to Wales from Cornwall, they can claim Welsh ancestry. Their grandmother was one of the many who left southern Wales to work in London dairies in the 1930s, and her mother was from Talgarth, an area that was well known in the past for its cheese.

Gorwydd Caerphilly is matured for at least two months and has time to develop a distinct rind as well as a superb rich flavour and creamy texture. The milk is obtained from nearby farms, and as the cheese is made from full-cream milk and matured in the traditional way, all the natural flavours are retained. Many years ago this type of Caerphilly was only made for the rich, or for special occasions. It is good that the Trethowans have resurrected this type of cheese, and have given today's consumer the opportunity to enjoy a mature traditional Caerphilly cheese.

Gorwydd Caerphilly is among the many Welsh cheeses that have won high acclaim in competition. In 2005 it was accorded the title of Best of British at the World Cheese Awards.

MERLIN CHEESES

Tourists have long associated Aberystwyth with the steep wooded valley of the Rheidol and Devil's Bridge. The Ystwyth valley lies almost parallel to the Rheidol valley and is of equal beauty. It is after the Ystwyth river that the University town is named. Tyn y Llwyn farm can be found on the slopes of the Ystwyth valley, off a single lane track from the mountain village of Pontrhydygroes.

Some twenty years ago, when Gill Pateman's eldest daughter developed an allergy to cow's milk, the family purchased a goat. As so often happens, one goat led to another, and when the family became fed up with eating rice pudding, it was a natural progression for this former home economics teacher to make cheese from the extra milk. This is how Merlin cheese was born.

As well as the plain mild and mature goat's cheese there is also a wide range of cheese with added ingredients, including apple, apricot, celery, mango or onion to name just a few of the more than twenty-five. These mini 200g cheeses are colourfully waxed and vacuum packed.

For the time being Merlin cheese is not available. It is only to be hoped that this situation will change soon.

Merlin Cheeses also act on behalf of Cheeses From Wales, providing a service to the small cheesemakers and customers who require a 'one-stop shop'.

TEIFI CHEESE

The Teifi river may be known by anglers for its salmon and sewin, but the valley is also rightly known for its excellent cheese.

Teifi Cheese was established in 1982 by John and Patrice Savage-Onstwedder and Paula van Werkhoven, all three of whom moved from Holland to Glynhynod about a year or so earlier. The area comprises rolling hills gently sloping towards the sea. As befits their Dutch heritage, the original cheese was made to a Dutch recipe using Dutch equipment. Glynhynod has only a small acreage and all the milk is obtained from nearby farmers. This local involvement ensures that the flavours found in the grass of the traditional meadows on which the cows graze pass into the cheese.

The original Teifi is sold as a young, fresh semi-hard smooth textured Gouda-style cheese, or as a matured product of some twelve months of age, by which time it has developed a distinct rich nutty flavour. A range of Teifi with additional ingredients – garlic, herbs, cumin and so forth – is also made, but it is for the 'washed rind' Celtic Promise that Glynhynod is so well known. The larger version, Saval, is a good cheese, but it has not achieved the same acclaim as its smaller brother.

The surface flora of Celtic Promise gives it a strong and to some an unpleasant smell, but this is the nature of this particular style of cheese. The flavour is delicate and aromatic and once tasted it is difficult to stop eating. Celtic Promise was supreme champion at the British Cheese Awards of 1998 and again in 2005.

A new dairy and farm shop are being built at Glynhynod to cope with the increasing demand for their cheese. The entrance to the new dairy has a distinct and individually designed stained-glass window made by John. Customers can be assured that the well-deserved reputation of Teifi Cheese will be upheld in this new dairy, as the same cheesemaking practices using Dutch equipment will continue in the new production and ripening areas.

CAWS CENARTH

The sudden imposition of milk quotas on all dairy farmers in April 1984 caused much concern. Initially for Gwynfor and Thelma Adams of Glyneithinog Farm, there seemed to be only two choices: either to pay a levy on what was regarded as over-production, or to tip the excess milk down the drain. However, they did have a third choice – to make cheese. This is how Caws Cenarth and the cheesemaking business was established in 1987.

Caws Teifi. Left: cheese in press. Right: large Teifi cheese in store. Note the clean shiny appearance typical of the cheese ready for despatch.

The families on both sides had some knowledge of making cheese. Gwynfor's grandmother had attended courses at Aberystwyth and, as often happened before the days of the Milk Marketing Board, when liquid milk was not required at the local factory it was taken home to be turned into cheese.

To the existing cheesemaking skills were added Thelma's marketing abilities, and soon Caws Cenarth was widely known in the most prestigious retail outlets. Gwynfor is rightly proud of his Holstein Friesian herd and the quality of the milk they produce. It took little effort to convert Glyneithinog to being an organic farm, and there is a plentiful supply of lush grassland and natural spring water, both vital elements in adding to the special flavour of the cheese.

Gwynfor and Thelma have been farming Glyneithinog for over forty years and have recently handed the cheese business over to their son Carwyn, who has shown a similar passion for cheese as his parents. The range has been expanded to include the mould-ripened Perl Wen, which has a white mould crust, and Perl Las, which has an internal blue mould. These are very different from the traditional Caerphilly and have already proved to be worthy and exciting additions to the range. The precious

Caws Cenarth maturing in storage

milk source still comes from the same herd of cows, but they are now being cared for by a neighbouring farmer, which gives Carwyn more time to devote to cheesemaking.

In the past, the tourist attractions of the area were the magnificent Cenarth Falls and the ancient art of coracle fishing. To these Caws Cenarth has now been added. Visitors can observe the cheesemaking process from a gallery, as well as sample and buy cheese at the farm shop.

CAWS CELTICA

The Ceri is a tributary of the Teifi and flows through a gently rolling countryside before joining the Teifi not far from Cenarth. Roger and Sue Hilditch moved to Capel Gwnda and started their sheep enterprise there in 1993. Sue is originally from Hampshire and Roger is a Lancastrian. Not surprisingly, both of them fell in love with the area.

Part of the farmstead can be traced back as far as 1747. A well on the site, which to date has provided an unbroken supply of water, is claimed to be holy and to have curative powers. The farm is not far from the coastline of Cardigan Bay, and the flock of around two hundred Friesland milking sheep enjoy the combination of sea breezes, rolling meadows and fresh spring water.

The late Olivia Mills, who founded the British Sheep Dairying Association, kindled the Hilditches' interest in sheep dairying and cheesemaking. Initially they produced milk for others to process, but in 1999 they launched their own range of sheep's cheese.

Sue makes the cheese in a compact, excellent dairy in one of the outbuildings on the farm. The plain Lammas is a typical Pecorino-style cheese. When young, it has a fresh creamy flavour, but is better when matured, by which time it has developed a lingering slightly sweet and nutty flavour. There is also a range of cheese with added ingredients. Beltane is a washed-curd cheese made in a similar way to Gouda, and left to mature for around twelve months. These matured cheeses are a real speciality, and are given the time to develop a very distinct rich flavour. It is no surprise that the Caws Celtica cheese has achieved considerable acclaim at national and international competitions.

LLANBOIDY CHEESEMAKERS

Cilowen is a typical western Wales farm situated in an area of wonderful rolling pastures. On a fine day the Preseli mountains can be seen in the distance. What makes this farm and the cheese that is made here so special, however, is the herd of rare breed Red Poll cows.

The cheesemaking business was started by Sue Jones in 1985, and since then Llanboidy cheese has achieved an international reputation. It is a small family business on a working farm. There is a separate and well-equipped dairy where the cheese is made, with the maturing room alongside. The milk for the Llanboidy range of cheese is passed directly from the milking parlour into the cheese dairy. It could not be more fresh and wholesome, retaining all the character of the milk produced by this ancient breed of cows.

More recently Cilowen organic cheese has been made on the farm. The milk for this cheese is supplied by nearby designated organic farms. This is a slightly softer, more creamy textured cheese than the Llanboidy type. The cheesemaking methods are traditional and all the cheeses are matured naturally, which allows the rinds to develop their characteristic appearance while in the store. All of this aids the individual flavour of each type of cheese.

A matured Llanboidy cheese has a firm smooth silky texture with a distinct almost spicy and robust mature flavour. It is equally acceptable as a young cheese, and is also available as a young cheese with laverbread as an added ingredient. Laverbread is an edible seaweed and a very popular food in southern Wales. While the most popular cheeses remain the plain Llanboidy and Cilowen, consumers also appreciate the other choices, with their added ingredients.

Both Llanboidy and Cilowen are highly sought-after cheeses, and are frequently to be found among the prize-winning entries in national and international shows.

PANT MAWR FARMHOUSE CHEESES

As you travel westwards towards Pembrokeshire, the rolling upland area of the Preseli mountains can be clearly seen. Pant Mawr is a small traditional farm situated in the Preseli foothills. Cynthia and David Jennings began the business in 1983, after they returned from Libya and North Yemen where they had been involved in commercial dairy enterprises. Pant Mawr is very much a family concern, which now also involves their son Jason.

A range of cow's and goat's milk cheese is made from locally-produced milk. The dairy is modern and well equipped but all the cheese is made by traditional methods and named after well known local landmarks. Caws Cerwyn, made from cow's milk, is an open-textured un-pressed cheese with a mild but buttery flavour. The older matured version of five to six months of age has a distinctive, full-bodied nutty flavour.

Caws y Graig, a hard goat cheese, varies in flavour according to whether it has been made from winter or summer milk. The summer milk cheese is firm-bodied with a distinct slightly sweet flavour, whereas that made from winter milk has a crumbly, almost chalky texture. These two cheeses reflect the seasons and clearly illustrate the attraction of small-scale farmhouse cheese, especially where consumers are seeking something natural and different. It is no wonder that Pant Mawr cheese has received gold awards at the World Cheese Awards.

It is not practical for visitors to see the cheesemaking process, but all the cheese varieties can be tasted at the farm shop. The shop also acts as the Post Office for the nearby village of Rosebush, and Cynthia acts as the postmistress on two mornings a week. This is a valuable facility in a rural area and is much appreciated by the local community.

LLANGLOFFAN FARMHOUSE CHEESE

The name Llangloffan is known throughout the world. It is a small hamlet a few miles from the north Pembrokeshire coast and can be found on any motorist atlas of the British Isles, listed as The Cheese Centre.

Joan and Leon Downey began making cheese at Llangloffan in 1977. Leon has made the cheese for the past twenty-eight years – first from his own small herd of Jersey cows, but more recently from the milk of a

Some of the Pant Mawr range of cheese

neighbouring farm. The cheese is only made when the cows are out in the fields and able to eat grass. The last cheese was made at Llangloffan on the 29th of October 2005, but others will continue making to Leon's recipe and initially with Leon's assistance.

The Llangloffan cheese recipe can be traced back to Leon's grandmother, who made a particular style of Cheshire cheese. It has a slight crumbly texture but with a wonderful full and lingering flavour. The coloured version is more typical of an old-fashioned Cheshire cheese.

Joan and Leon Downey have been exponents of raw milk cheese and have been prominent in reviving the art of traditional farmhouse practices. On occasion this has brought Leon into conflict with people who have little understanding of the process of cheesemaking, and this and increasing bureaucratic controls on all food manufacturers has had some bearing on his decision to retire.

Leon was principal viola player at the Halle Orchestra before he and Joan bought Llangloffan in 1976, and he has never lost his passion for music. The cheese centre, shop and restaurant will continue at Llangloffan, while Leon will have more time to devote to his music, conducting and encouraging those of all ages to share in his enthusiasm.

Llangloffan cheese

CAWS CAERFAI

The city of St Davids in Pembrokeshire is named after the patron saint of Wales and is the smallest city in Britain. Nearby there are several small bays with steep cliffs facing St Brides Bay. One of these, Caerfai Bay, is a lovely sandy cove with fascinating rock pools. The long coastline has both dramatic scenery and wonderful lush pastures. Many of these pastures have mixtures of coastal grasses that add to the flavour of milk and cheese produced from cattle grazing here. The climate is mild and the cows can be out grazing from early spring to December.

Wyn Evans' parents and grandparents farmed Caerfai before him, but it was in 1991 that Wyn and Christine Evans began to farm the place organically. With the help and under the guidance of Dougal Campbell they started making cheese in 1994. The original Caerfai Cheddar was similar in style to the Tyn Grug cheese made by Dougal. Wyn acknowledges that he owes much to Dougal and it is good that Dougal's philosophy and expertise continues.

Caerfai is very much a family business, with holiday cottages as well as cheesemaking bringing in income. Nowadays, a new generation is involved in making the cheese with their father's help. The aim at Caerfai is to generate enough of their own electricity to be self sufficient, and to make a batch of cheese using only renewable energy. A mix of solar panels, ground heat, a wind turbine on the coastal head, a digester utilising the slurry from the cattle (which in itself is equivalent to about three gallons of fuel oil) all contribute towards this aim of self sufficiency using alternative energy sources.

Most of the cheese made at Caerfai – Cheddar, Caerphilly and Caerphilly with leeks – is sold locally. This area relies heavily on its tourist trade, and while Caerfai cheese has gained many accolades in competition, the best accolade is a repeat purchase.

QUIRT FARM

The island of Anglesey is well known for the quality of its pastures and its cattle. It is a fertile land with a plentiful supply of grass and a mild climate. Quirt Farm lies by the Menai Straits and benefits from the additional shelter found in that area of the island. This enables Richard Davies to use the New Zealand system of having his cows grazing outside throughout the year.

There are about a hundred Friesian and some Friesian-Jersey-cross milking cows at Quirt, and like many another farmhouse manufacturer, cheesemaking began at Quirt more by accident than design. Huw, one of Margaret and Richard's children, was required to research a project as part of his course at the University of Wales Bangor. He chose farm cheesemaking, and this triggered a wider family interest. Margaret attended a short course at Coleg Menai in 2001, from where the first commercial batches of Gorau Glas were made in 2002.

Gorau Glas is a 400g cheese with an internal blue mould and a blue-green surface mould that gives a wonderfully well balanced full flavour. The texture is soft and creamy. A 200g smaller version called Babi Glas is just as good. Gorau Glas was entered in the class for new cheese varieties at the 2002 British Cheese awards, and was awarded gold to great acclaim.

The production facilities at nearby Coleg Menai were used for a while, but the cheese was matured at the farm. Nowadays there is a well-equipped self-contained dairy in one of the outbuildings, and all the production is carried out at Quirt Farm itself. This diversification has involved all the family.

KNOLTON FARM

Cheshire cheese has been a recognised variety from very early cheesemaking days. The English counties of Cheshire and Shropshire, together with the Vale of Clwyd in Wales, were associated with Cheshire cheese even before Roman times. Although there are still farms making Cheshire cheese in this border area, the Latham family of Knolton Farm are now the only farmhouse cheesemakers on the Welsh side of the border who continue the tradition.

Little notice has been taken of the actual border between England and Wales as far as farming and cheesemaking is concerned. Mrs Eileen Latham, whose mother came from the Welsh side of the border near Welshpool, was born in 1915 at Longford Grange, Market Drayton, Shropshire and moved to Knolton Farm with her husband Robert (Bob) in 1940. Mrs Latham is a remarkable lady and has recorded not only her family history but also that of her husband's family who have lived in and around Overton on Dee for several centuries.

It was wartime when Mr and Mrs Latham moved into Knolton Farm, a period of severe restrictions, and it was not until 1955 that they decided to make cheese again. Bob Latham became a member of the Cheshire Cheese Federation and in June of that year he received his first cheese payment of £452.9.1d, a great improvement on the £349 for the previous milk payment.

Mrs Latham describes the heartrending effects of the Foot and Mouth Disease outbreaks in the area, the first in 1960 and the second in 1967. The resilience of the farming community is evident in her writing, and it is also evident in the continued making of cheese in the area.

While researching Latham family history, Mrs Latham found various family records illustrating the importance of cheese in the area. The inventory of 'Goods and Chattels' of Robert Latham, who died on the 4th of April 1733, include the following entries:

10 cows valued at	£30. 0.0d
A cheese press	18.0d
4 cheese vats	15.0d
A parcel of cheese	18. 0.0d

It does not say how much cheese was contained in the parcel but it was evidently a substantial amount.

Mr Jonathan Latham (son of Eileen and Robert Latham), with his wife Russel now runs the cheesemaking and selling business. More cheese varieties are being made, as well as other dairy ingredients, but the most successful product is Mrs Latham's lemon curd, which derives from a recipe originally made for Napoleon III. This is very much a winner at the various farmers' markets in northern Wales and across the border in Chester.

PLAS FARM LTD.

American-style Cottage cheese is generally thought of as being an industrial product that is made in large quantities. However it can be made on a smaller farmhouse scale and was developed in this way at Plas Farm on the island of Anglesey, using organic milk.

Other products of dairy and non-dairy origin were developed, and in 1988 production was moved from the farm to the present location on a nearby industrial site. The company produces a range of natural and flavoured organic cream cheese in both retail and catering sizes in addition to the cottage cheese.

Plas Farm also makes a range of dairy ice creams, frozen desserts based on milk, coleslaw and potato salads, along with other health foods.

PONT GÂR (CARMARTHENSHIRE CHEESE COMPANY LTD)

The Carmarthenshire Cheese Company Ltd was formed early in 2006 and the first cheese was made on the 1st of April at the Food Park, Horeb, Llandysul. Sian Elin and Steve Peace have many years of experience in the dairy industry, especially the cheesemaking side of the industry. The opportunity arose for them to use two advance food units at the Food Park, where equipment has been installed to make and mature a range of soft cheese using white and blue mould cultures.

The milk comes from a local producer, which makes it possible to ensure the quality and authenticity of supply. The soft cheeses will be marketed under the Pont Gâr brand. They are made in the traditional way and, as I can testify, having tasted some of the first production, they are a delicious addition to the range of Welsh mould-ripened cheese.

Llangloffan cheese is also to be made at this site under the guiding hands of Leon Downey. This will ensure that the recipe will continue to be used, its quality ensured, and that Llangloffan will not become a lost variety of Welsh cheese.

The plan is to move production from the Food Park to a farm site within the next three years. In the meanwhile, the Food Park provides valuable experience in both making and marketing new varieties of Welsh cheese.

HAFOD CHEESE

This is a new venture by Sam and Rachel Holden at their family farm near Llangybi. Bwlchwernen Fawr is the oldest established organic dairy farm in Wales. Its herd of Ayrshire cows produces rich creamy milk well suited to the making of a hard cheese.

Sam has been making cheese with Simon Jones of Lincolnshire

Poacher fame, who learnt his cheesemaking with Dougal Campbell. There are no longer any teaching centres in Wales, so it is good to know the craft of cheesemaking continues to be handed on, and in this instance returns from England to Wales. The name 'Hafod' evokes the ancient Welsh tradition of moving to a summer grazing location, and the meadowland at Bwlchwernen on which the cows graze provides wonderful natural flavours in the milk and the cheese.

Hafod will be a hard cheese, made from unpasteurised cow's milk and matured for at least nine months. Production should commence before the end of 2006.

CAWS MYNYDD DU

The tradition of making a Caerphilly style cheese in the Talgarth area has recently been revived. Helen and Andrew Meredith began making cheese from their flock of Poll Dorset and Poll Dorset crosses in November 2005. At first their milk was sent to others to make ice cream but there was a tradition of cheesemaking in Andrew's family and after finding the old cheese press and other equipment they could not resist reviving the craft. Lodge Farm lies within the Brecon Beacons National Park and it has taken a while to satisfy the sometimes conflicting demands of the Park and today's manufacturing requirements.

A barn has been converted to make and store the cheese. It is a Caerphilly type, matured for around 8 weeks in the cellar of he farmhouse and made in two sizes – a three and half kilo wheel and a smaller 1kg cheese. This is a welcome addition to the sheep milk varieties.

Chapter 8

Where to buy Welsh cheese

All the creameries sell their cheese under brand names and these can be found at major supermarket outlets. The source of these brands are clearly indicated on the labels – such as Afon Cleddau (Haverfordwest Cheese Ltd.), Welsh Gold (Aeron Valley Cheese), Cadog (Dairy Farmers of Britain, Llandyrnog), and Old Shire (South Caernarfon Creameries Ltd. Chwilog).

Other well known brands such as the Snowdonia range of cheese can be purchased at supermarkets, specialist shops and via their website www.snowdoniacheese.co.uk. For information on the delicious premium Collier's Cheddar visit their website www.collierscymreig.com.

Cheeses from Wales was set up as a Limited Company to faciliate the

SCC's co-operative shop on the Maes, Pwllheli in the 1980s

purchase of a wide selection of Welsh cheese from one source. Cheese can be supplied to any area within the UK. They may be contacted at:

Cheeses from Wales Ltd.
Tyn-y-Llwyn
Pontrhydygroes
Ystrad Meurig
Ceredigion SY25 6DP
Tel: 01239 891574
Email: enquiries@cheesesfromwales.co.uk

Welsh farmhouse cheese can be purchased from many specialist shops, from farm shops, at food fairs, at farmers' markets and at agricultural shows. These offer local and regional produce at its best, most of which cannot be found in the supermarkets. Specialist farmhouse cheese will vary in flavour and may not be available at all times of the year. As a natural product it will reflect the seasons and the craft of the cheesemaker.

Many of the hotels in Wales promote local produce and Welsh cheese. Wholesalers such as Caws Cymru and Blas ar Fwyd distribute Welsh cheese throughout Wales. It is worth asking for Welsh cheese when you next go out for a meal: the cheesemakers need consumers in order to be able to continue as economically viable units, and their future lies with you.

The last churns delivered to SSC Chwilog by Brian Lowther, Pencraig, Llanarmon in 1996. Official figures indicate that by 1980 all milk from the farms of Wales was collected in tankers but it was possible for special arrangements to be made at a Farmer's Co-operative.

A 1960s creamery. Above: cheese in the process of being textured. Blocks being turned to aid the process. Below: mechanical cutting of the blocks before turning again. The texture changes from a mat of crumbs to that resembling chicken breast.

BIBLIOGRAPHY

Cheke, V. *The Story of Cheesemaking in Britain* (London: Routledge & Kegan Paul, 1959).

Elias, T. *Cattle/Gwartheg* (Llanrwst: Gwasg Carreg Gwalch, 2000).

Evans, J. *Letters written during a tour through South Wales* (London: Board of Agriculture Review on State of Agriculture in Glamorganshire, 1804).

———. *The Beauties of England and Wales* Vol. XVII, Part I (1812).

Fox, J. *General View of the Agriculture of the County of Glamorgan* (London: Board of Agriculture Review on State of Agriculture in Wales, 1794).

Hassall, C. *General View of the Agriculture of the County of Carmarthen* (London: Board of Agriculture Review on State of Agriculture in Wales, 1794).

———. *General View of the Agriculture of the County of Pembrokeshire*. (London: Board of Agriculture Review on State of Agriculture in Wales, 1794).

Hughes, H. *An Uprooted Community: a History of Epynt* (Llandysul: Gomer, 1998).

Hughes, J. 'Cosynnau Caws Cernyw', *Y Gadlas* 2.4-5 (Mai-Mehefin 1977).

Latham, E. *My Three Score Years and Ten* (private publication, 1985).

Lewis, J. 'Some aspects of the History and Development of Dairying in Cardiganshire' (Thesis: University of Wales, 1948).

Kay, G. *General View of the Agriculture of North Wales* (Board of Agriculture Review on State of Agriculture in Wales, 1794).

Rance, P. *The Great British Cheese Book* (London: Macmillan, 1982).

Reed, C. S. 'On the Farming of South Wales', *Journal of the Agricultural Society of England* X , Article VI 122 (1849).

Tibbott, M. 'Cheese-Making in Glamorgan', *Journal of Ethnological Studies* 34 (1995-1996): pp. 64-79.

Vieth P. 'Micro-organisms and their Action on Milk & Milk Products', *Journal of the Royal Society of England* 23 (1887): pp. 374-402.

Wall, Barrow W. 'The Agriculture of Pembrokeshire', *Journal of the Royal Society of England* 23 (1887): p. 70.

Williams, J. Gwynn. *The University College of North Wales: Foundations 1884-1927* (Cardiff: University of Wales Press, 1985).

University College of North Wales Calendar for the Year 1892-3 Part II, 'Out-College Work in Agriculture'.

Producers and suppliers of Welsh Cheese

BLAS AR FWYD

Delicatessen, wine shop
and Welsh cheese
wholesaler
Heol yr Orsaf
Llanrwst
LL26 0BT
Tel: 01492 640215
Fax: 01492 642215
Email: info@blasarfwyd.com
Website: www.blasarfwyd.com
Contact: Deiniol ap Dafydd
and Chandra Dafydd

CASTLE DAIRIES

Pontygwindy Industrial Estate
Caerphilly
Gwent CF83 3HU
Tel: 02920 883981
Fax: 02920886506
Email: Nigel@castledairies.co.uk
Contact: Nigel Lloyd
Visitors: by appointment only
Website: www.castledairies.co.uk

ABERGAVENNY FINE FOODS LTD.
Castle Meadows Park
Abergavenny, NP7 7RZ
Tel: 01873 850001 Fax: 01873 850002
Email: brysonc@abergavenny.co.uk
Contact: Bryson Craske
Visitors: by appointment only

CAWS PANTYSGAWN

NANTYBWLA FARM
College Road
Carmarthen, SA31 3QS
Tel: 01267 237905
Contact: Edward Morgan
Visitors: by appointment
only

CILWR FARM
Talyllychau
Llandeilo
Carmarthenshire, SA19 7BQ
Tel: and Fax: 01558 685555
Email: goat@homested.fsbusiness.co.uk
Contact: Richard Beard
Visitors: by appointment only

HUFENFA DE ARFON
Rhydygwystl
Chwilog
Gwynedd, LL53 6SB
Tel: 01766 810251 Fax: 01766 810578 Email: mail@sccwales.co.uk
Website: www.sccwales.co.uk

92

TRETHOWAN'S DAIRY LTD.

Gorwydd Farm
Llanddewi Brefi
Tregaron
Ceredigion, SY25 6NY
Tel: 01570 493516
Fax: 01570 493274
Email:
enquiries@trethowansdairy.co.uk
Contact: Maugan Trethowan
Visitors: by appointment only
Website: www.gorwydd.com

MERLIN CHEESES

Pontrhydygroes
Ystrad Meurig
Ceredigion, SY25 6DP
Tel: 01239 891574
Fax: 07813 876013
Email: enquiries@cheesesfromwales.co.uk
Contact: Gill Pateman
Visitors: by appointment only

COLLIER'S

Cheddar Pwerus Cymreig
Powerful Welsh Cheddar
Fayrefields Foods Ltd.
P.O. Box 89
Crickhowell NP8 1XF
www.collierscymreig.com

TEIFI FARMHOUSE CHEESE
Glynhynod
Ffostrasol
Llandysul
Ceredigion, SA44 5JY
Tel: 01239 851528
Fax: 01239 851528
Email: john@teificheese.com
Contact: John Savage
Visitors: dairy by appointment only
Farm shop on site

CAWS CENARTH
Fferm Glyneithinog
Pontseli
Boncath
Ceredigion, SA37 0LH
Tel: 01239 710432
Fax: 01239 710432
Email: cenarth.cheese@virgin.net
Contact: Carwyn Adams
Visitors: welcome in the observation gallery. Farm shop on site.
Website: www.welshorganiccheese.com

LLANBOIDY CHEESEMAKERS
Cilowen Uchaf Farm
Login
Whitland
Carmarthenshire, SA34 0TJ
Tel: 01994 448303
Fax: 01994 448303
Email: sue@llanboidycheese.co.uk
Contact: Sue Jones
Visitors: by appointment only
Website:
www.llanboidycheese.co.uk

KNOLTON FARMHOUSE CHEESE LTD.
Overton-on-Dee
Wrexham, LL13 0LG
Tel: 01978 710221
Fax: 01978 710821
Contact: Jonathan Latham

PANT MAWR FARMHOUSE CHEESES
Rosebush
Clunderwen
Pembrokeshire, SA66 7QU
Tel: 01437 532627
Fax: 01437 532627
Email: david@pantmawrcheeses.co.uk
Contact: David Jennings
Visitors: by appointment only
Farm shop on site
Website: www.pantmawrcheeses.co.uk

LLANGLOFFAN FARMHOUSE CHEESE

Castle Morris
Haverfordwest
Pembrokeshire, SA62 5ET
Tel: 01348 891241
Fax: 0870 0558 159
Email: admin@welshcheese.co.uk
Contact: Leon Downey
Visitors: farm shop and
restaurant on site
Website: www.welshcheese.co.uk

CAWS CAERFAI

Caerfai Farm
St. David's
Haverfordwest
Pembrokeshire, SA62 5QT
Tel: 01437 720548
Fax: 01437 720548
Contact: Wyn Evans
Visitors: by appointment only
Farm shop on site
Website: www.caerfai.co.uk

CAWS CELTICA
Capel Gwnda
Rhydlewis
Llandysul
Ceredigion, SA44 5RN
Tel: 01239 851419   Fax: 01239 851419
Email: info@cawsceltica-farmhousecheese.co.uk
Contact: Sue Hilditch
Visitors: by appointment only
Website: www.cawsceltica-farmhousecheese.co.uk

QUIRT FARM
Dwyran
Anglesey, LL61 6BZ
Tel: 01248 430570
Email: rodavies2001@yahoo.com
Contact: Margaret Davies
Visitors: by appointment only

SNOWDONIA CHEESE

Unit B6
Trem y Dyffryn
Colomendy Industrial
Estate
Denbigh LL16 5TX
Tel: 01745 813388
Fax: 01745 813550
Website: www.snowdonia-
cheese.co.uk

HAFOD CHEESE
Bwlchwernen Fawr
Llangybi
Lampeter, SA48 8PS
Tel: 01570 493427
Email: SamuelHolden@hotmail.com
Contact: Samuel Holden

CAWS CYMRU
Wervile Grange
Pentregat
Plwmp
SA44 6HW
Tel: 01239 654800
Contact: Richard Harris and
Theo Bond

CAWS MYNYDD DU
Lodge Farm
Talgarth
Brecon, LD3 0DP
Tel: 01874 711812
Contact:
Andrew and Helen Meredith
Email: Meredith@swi.co.uk

PLAS FARM LTD
Celtic House
Gaerwen
Anglesey
Gwynedd, LL60 6HR
Tel: 01248 422011
Fax: 01248 422003
Email: plas@anchor.co.uk
Contact: David Williams
Visitors: by appointment only

CARMARTHENSHIRE CHEESE COMPANY LTD.
Boksburg Hall
Llanllwch
Carmarthenshire, SA31 3RN
Tel: 01267 221168
Email: datryssolutions@btinternet.com
Contact: Steve Peace
Visitors: to Food Park by appointment only

LLWYNHELYG FARM SHOP

Farm shop which specialises in stocking a wide variety of Welsh Cheese

Sarnau
Llandysul
Ceredigion,
SA44 6QU
Tel: 01239 811079
Contact:
Teifi and Jenny
Davies

FARMERS' MARKETS IN WALES

www.fmiw.co.uk

An useful website listing the latest information about where and when the markets are taking place – which have Welsh cheese stalls almost without exception. It also links to individual markets' websites.